2

GAMES
for the
SUPER-INTELLIGENT

GAMES
for the
SUPER-INTELLIGENT

JAMES F. FIXX

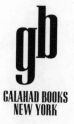

GALAHAD BOOKS
NEW YORK

CONTENTS

CONTENTS

Games for the
Superintelligent

Oct. 1999

Dad,

**For my father,
who started me wondering**

Sounds like his dad was
a lot like mine.
Thanks for the wonderful
gift of questioning.
Happy Birthday,
Love,
Tk

Confessions of
a thoroughly puzzled man

For as long as I can remember I have taken a special—some might say an almost irrational—delight in puzzles, games, and problems of all sorts. At one time I devised, or at least tried to devise, formulas for some wondrously worthless calculations— for predicting with what frequency an automobile odometer would show a symmetrical number, such as 00100 or 50505 or 99999, for finding the sum of a string of consecutive numbers, for computing the interrelationship of speed, spin, direction, and depth of a crosscourt backhand (that one, somehow, never worked out very well). And I can still remember how I felt, while taking a college physics course, when the professor wrote on the blackboard a formidably complicated formula that turned out, as soon as one understood it, to be absolutely startling in its elegance and simplicity. I knew, at that moment, that I was looking on beauty bare.

The feeling I experienced at that time, though I can no longer even remember what the formula was, has never left me. I am still awed and fascinated by any really good mathematical morsel, and I confess to such indefensible aberrations as having once ridden a train far past my stop while trying to figure out why a dozen or so apparently quite practical perpetual motion machines described in *Scientific American* wouldn't work. (Curse you, Gerald Piel!) This, then, is the book of a thoroughly committed man, a True Believer when it comes to a certain variety of mental shenanigans.

What, exactly, is that variety? Well, as will be seen, the puzzles in this book all require little or no real expertise. Some of them look forbiddingly intricate, but you have my word that none of them really are that way. You don't need to be a nuclear physicist to solve any of them, and it is very likely, in fact, that if you happen to *be* a nuclear physicist, some of the puzzles will prove more troublesome than if you were less heavily burdened with mathematical sophistication.

No, what these puzzles all have is a kind of do-it-with-mirrors difficulty, a difficulty much more spurious than actual. And that's precisely what makes them the charming diversions they are. They all require some logical (or, on occasion, illogical) leap that, in human terms, is the rough equivalent of a monkey in a cage suddenly realizing that it needs to use a stick to reach a banana. No stick, no banana. And so it is here: No leap, no solution. If that seems obscure now, it won't take you long to see what is meant.

A book like this would have been all but impossible to compile and write had I not by chance stumbled onto a sort of mother lode of puzzles and puzzlers: an organization called Mensa, which has recruited its entire membership from the most intelligent 2 per cent of the population. Several years ago, upon first attending a Mensa meeting in order to write a magazine article about the group, I was startled when at meeting's end several M's, as they call themselves, got together over beer and pretzels not to tell bawdy stories or any other such thing but—*mirabile dictu!*—to swap puzzles with each other. It did not, however, occur to me until much later that there might be the makings of a book in the puzzle phenomenon. When it finally did, Mensa members—who are, among other things, the most certifiably superintelligent group in existence today—were of incalculable assistance. To solicit their help was to open a floodgate that kept me busily reading letters and, in more cases than one, scratching my head in happy puzzlement over their suggestions for many, many months. (The names of some of those from whom I have shamelessly stolen ideas appear at the end of this book.)

Lest I be charged with a singlemindedness I do not even begin to possess, I should perhaps mention that puzzling is far from the only thing I do, nor is it even *most* of what I do. And that's undoubtedly just as well, to judge by the look of glazed stupefaction that occasionally creeps over the faces of people whose patience and kindly pretense are beginning to fray. (To some people, it seems, too many puzzles are like too many home movies.) No, puzzles are something the aficionado does in odd, wonderful moments, mostly alone, and he is very lucky indeed when on occasion he finds himself with an equally devoted partner-in-puzzles. Since there aren't many of us—compared, say, to hockey or baseball fans—it doesn't happen often.

So a very special welcome.

JAMES F. FIXX

Riverside, Connecticut

Contents

I.

The pleasures of intelligence—
and some incidental perils

Practically all of us, whether we're bright or dull, tend to take it for granted that intelligence is a Good Thing and a lack of intelligence a Bad Thing—period. A little reflection will show, however, that it's not nearly that simple. Though very bright people seldom receive much sympathy for their brightness—a little incidental derision maybe, but not sympathy—they suffer along under handicaps undreamed of by their less gifted brethren. Nor are these, as one might suppose, simply the burdens imposed by a heightened awareness, a greater sense of life's complexities, a more poetic and sensitively tuned soul, etc., etc., etc. They are, on the contrary, provably distressing in quite practical ways—ways that bedevil virtually all those whose I.Q.s have never learned to play possum.

The problems of the superintelligent take a number of forms, but whatever they are they almost always start early. The following conversation, between a second-grade teacher and a bright pupil, is a cogently chilling case in point:

TEACHER: I am going to read you a series of numbers: 1, 2, 3, 4, 5, 6, 7. Now, which of those numbers can be divided evenly by 2?

PUPIL: All of them.

TEACHER: Try again. And this time, *think.*

PUPIL (after a pause): All of them.

TEACHER: All right, how do you divide 5 evenly by 2?

PUPIL: Two and a half and two and a half.

TEACHER: If you're going to be smart-alecky, you can leave the room.

The story is, I am sorry to say, a true one. So is the story of the high school student who was asked on an examination to describe a method for finding the height of a building by using a barometer. The student, bright enough to be bored by the obvious answer, decided to describe not one but two alternate methods. Take the barometer, he wrote, and drop it from the top of the building, timing the interval until you see it smash on the ground. Then, using the standard formula for acceleration of a falling object, calculate the height of the building. Or, he went on, find the owner of the building and say to him, "If you'll tell me how tall your building is I'll give you a good barometer." At last report the student was in deep trouble with his school's administrative hierarchy.

Intelligence is, of course, not a problem just to the young. A study at the University of Michigan revealed that executives with high I.Q.s are as likely to create problems as to solve them—to stumble over their own brains, as one report expressed it. Businessmen with only average I.Q.s, on the other hand, being less apt to confuse themselves with a multiplicity of factors, are often much better problem solvers.

Similarly, psychologist Max L. Fogel, a specialist in intelligence, reports that his studies of Mensa members reveal that being unusually bright can be a distinct problem. "As a group," he writes, "they tend to change jobs more often and encounter more difficulties and dissatisfactions than the general population. This is partly a function of their own personality problems, but it frequently also derives from the belligerence and hostility

12

of employers, peers, and subordinates. Another factor is boredom with established routine and insufficiently creative demands required by vocational responsibilities. . . . Many Mensa members learned to adapt by repressing or disguising their intellectual interests."

Intelligence can cause trouble, too, by teasing the mind into supposing it can solve problems that in fact may defy solution. One bright man, a person who on occasion enjoys a drink or two, addressed himself to the problem of losing weight while continuing to drink, with, in his own words, the following results:

"Losing weight, of course, is a matter of burning up more calories than you take in. A calorie, as everyone knows, is defined as 'the amount of heat required to raise the temperature of one gram of water one degree centigrade.'

"Let us take a good glass of Scotch and soda. Since a gram of water is pretty close to 1 cc (to make it simple), put in plenty of ice and fill it up to about six or seven ounces, making it, say, 200 cc. Since it contains melting ice, its temperature must be 0° centigrade (neglecting the temperature-lowering effect of the alcohol, Scotch, and gas).

"Sooner or later the body must furnish 7400 calories (200 cc $\times 37°$ C.) to bring it up to body temperature. Since the calorie-counter books show Scotch as 100 calories per shot, and club soda as 0 calories, we should be able to sit around all day, drinking Scotch and soda, and losing weight like mad.

"P.S.: I tried this and it didn't work." So much for the power of pure reason.

On the other hand, being bright does have some undeniable pleasures, and it is one especially beguiling subspecies of those pleasures that this book is all about.

But how can you tell whether these mental pushups and deep

13

knee bends are for you? And how serious a symptom is it if they aren't?

It's a good idea, first of all, to remember that intelligence isn't any single, readily definable quality. On the contrary, it is a complicated assortment of qualities. Some of us possess some of them, some of us others. Columnist Sidney J. Harris has long campaigned against intelligence tests on precisely those grounds—that too many of them treat intelligence as if it were a single identifiable thing, like red hair or double-jointed thumbs. He writes: "We have categorized and stereotyped people for too long by conventional I.Q. tests, which are misleading and inaccurate. Even Binet, the inventor of the first such test, when asked point-blank what intelligence was, replied with cynical candor, 'It is what my test measures.' Of course, as he knew, this is a circular and meaningless definition." Harris, pointing out that a newly devised British test measures six separate abilities (reasoning, verbal ability, spatial perception, number ability, memory, and something called ideational fluency), goes on to say: "I should not be complaining about I.Q. tests because my kind of intelligence does best at them—the highly verbal intelligence. But, knowing how dumb I am in some other important areas of life, it seems to me that the single-score test is profoundly unfair to other equally useful kinds of intelligence. Its abolition can go a long way toward releasing children from the tyranny of a senseless number."

As Harris indicates, a person may possess one mental ability in sharply heightened form but nevertheless be perfectly average in other respects. (Or even, for that matter, considerably below average. Consider the curious case of so-called idiots savants— the hospital patient with the 60 I.Q. who can beat doctors, psychologists, and technicians at checkers, the man with the 29 I.Q. who can instantly calculate the day of the week for any date from

1959 to 1979, or the man with the 30 I.Q. who, having heard any song once, can play it flawlessly on his guitar.) So if you don't particularly enjoy the kind of puzzles and problems we're talking about here, that fact alone says nothing about your intelligence in general. It merely means that you don't have the proper sort of mind for them and that, bright though you may be, you will be happier sticking to bridge, Monopoly, or whatever your special intellectual addiction is. No hard feelings.

But what, exactly, *is* the proper sort of mind? And how do you know if yours is one of them?

Let's start by taking a look at a few of the minds that unquestionably are the sort we are talking about.

Bostock Hackett III, one of the people who contributed to this book, certainly has such a mind. In a letter, he writes of the "thrill" of mental exercise. "In the same manner that an athlete enjoys his conditioning and the feeling of satisfaction that comes from being in shape," he observes, "I have seen [bright people] deliberately create a faster game of Ping Pong in their conversations. The difference between their conversations and those of so-called average people is in the speed, quickness, and agility of the replies." (For some time Hackett has been trying to drum up interest in some sort of "Mental Olympics"—he doesn't specify exactly how it might work—but so far has found no takers.)

Easy Sloman qualifies, too. Here's the kind of thing he enjoys puzzling over:

What is the next letter in the following sequence:

O T T F F S S? (Chapter I, Question 1*)

"That," Sloman says, "is the kind of question I like best. The most fun is not in simple cerebration but in exercising the kind of sideways approach to logic that is not reducible to formula."

---

* Answers to puzzles begin on page 78.

An illuminating description of the same phenomenon—the sideways approach—occurs in Arthur Koestler's book *The Act of Creation*. Discussing what happens when no apparent solution to a problem exists, when there is, as he calls it, a "blocked situation," he writes: "When all hopeful attempts at solving the problem by traditional methods have been exhausted, thought runs around in circles . . . like rats in a cage. Next, the matrix of organized, purposeful behavior itself seems to go to pieces, and random trials make their appearance, accompanied by tantrums and attacks of despair—or by the distracted absentmindedness of the creative obsession. That absentmindedness is, of course, in fact singlemindedness; for at this stage—the 'period of incubation'—the whole personality, down to the unverbalized and unconscious layers, has become saturated with the problem. . . . This condition remains until either chance or intuition provides a link to a quite different matrix." It is then, and only then, that the problem can be solved.

Some people seem to have a greater talent than others for exercising this sort of sideways logic—for thinking in quite unexpected and essentially unchartable ways. Colin Carmichael, writing in the magazine *Design*, tells the story—it recalls, in a way, our earlier barometer story—of a class of engineering students who were given the following question on an exam: How long should a three-pound beef roast stay in a 325-degree oven for the center to reach a temperature of 150 degrees? One student, described as a "Big Project man," didn't come up with an answer but did offer a plan for a series of precise experiments that would yield an accurate answer in six to nine months. Another student, an advocate of the practical approach, went out and bought a roast, an oven thermometer, and a watch. He wrote his report while munching medium-rare roast beef sandwiches. A third student used logic. Reasoning that ani-

16

mal tissue is mostly water and therefore should have about the same specific heat and conductivity, he applied heat transfer theory to produce his answer (it proved, incidentally, to be quite close to that of the second student). The quickest answer, however, came from a student who called up his mother on the phone and got the answer from her. "Which of these men," asks Mr. Carmichael, "promises to be the most effective engineer?"

What we are talking about is aptly expressed in William P. Hull's description of the thinker: "His delight is in ideas." Many people, for example, find delight in curious logical relationships—such as the oddly useless sign bearing these words:

KEEP OFF THIS SIGN

Or by the card with the intriguing words on both sides. On one side is written:

THE STATEMENT ON THE OTHER SIDE OF THIS
CARD IS FALSE.

And on the other side:

THE STATEMENT ON THE OTHER SIDE OF THIS
CARD IS TRUE.

(In somewhat the same vein, when Leo Tolstoy and his brother were children they used to pretend that any wish they made would come true if they could stand in a corner and not think of a white bear.)

A student named Norris F. Krueger, Jr., delights in ideas, too—with a sly and cunning difference. "I have a little game I play," he writes. "It's called 'Beat the Establishment.' It goes like this: Someone poses a situation utterly impossible to

17

solve—then we solve it. Sometimes it's a physical problem, like how to retrieve a pencil from some difficult place (such as my principal's office). Sometimes it's purely mental (along the lines of the old argument about how many angels could stand on the head of a pin). This game combines brain-storming, group therapy, and high adventure. (Note: One ground rule is that we proceed through 100 per cent legal methods—no crime, just sneakiness.)"

Or consider the kind of game represented by the apparently simple question:

How many times does the digit 9 appear from 1 to 100? (Puzzle 2)

Think carefully. No, the answer isn't 10. It isn't even 11. If that one has a certain charm for you—and if you stick with it long enough to discover the "hidden" 9's—you're one of us.

Finally, consider the following diagram:

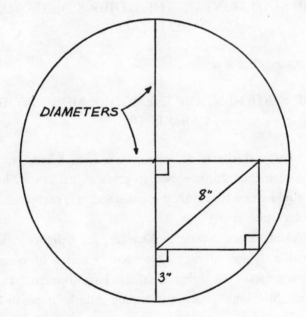

The problem: To find the radius of the circle. (Puzzle 3)

"This problem intrigues me," writes E. C. Hanford, "because the elementary answer is so often reduced to its most complicated form."

This phenomenon—making inherently simple things complicated—is one that has frequently been observed where the minds of very bright people are concerned. Many problems are in fact quite simple but are made difficult because they look, somehow, as if they just *ought* to be difficult, or because the mind is lured into concentrating on an irrelevant aspect of the problem. (I remember, as a child, my wonderment upon first encountering the bus trick: You are told that a bus starts out in the morning with no passengers. At the first stop, three passengers get on. At the next stop, one gets off and two get on. At the next, two get off and one gets on. And so on through several more stops—at which point you are asked: "How many times did the bus stop?")

Jim Cochrane, a particularly inventive puzzle specialist, writes: "There seems to be an interesting class of problematical recreations which, while mathematical in nature, tend to elude the mathematician more often than the non-mathematician. The characteristic of such problems is that they are amenable to solution through methodical application of mathematical tools and techniques, but also may be solved via a short-cut route. The trained mathematician is likely to attack the problem as a specific case of a general problem he has been trained to solve. A child, lacking powerful mathematical tools, is more apt to find the short-cut solution if there is one, since he is forced to take a fresh and creative view. The ability to find the quick solution is probably related to creativity."

A person's feelings about puzzles and games like these are, I

19

think, a fairly reliable touchstone to the presence or absence of certain qualities of mind. If you find that you like them, if they give you an indefinable but quite wonderful sense of pleasure, then you're no doubt right for this book. And it, with luck, will be right for you.

II.

Puzzles and games to start going quietly crazy by

The typical puzzle, especially the kind most admired by the superintelligent, has its roots in mathematics, in one or another variety of logic, or in words, or it may be based on a combination of these. The puzzles in this chapter, intended as an introduction to the fine art of puzzlemanship, offer a pleasantly maddening *mélange* of those three elements. Practically all of them, incidentally, are from the personal collections of people who are brighter than 98 per cent of the population. So be forewarned: Few of them are easy. But they do constitute a useful Baedeker to the landscape of puzzling.

Let's begin with a couple of quick ones (but not necessarily easy ones):

1. Match Tricks

(a) Make the following equation correct by moving only one match:

$$\frac{XXIII}{VII} = II$$

(b) And the following:

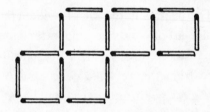

2. Squares and Triangles

Make two squares and four triangles from eight matches, without breaking or bending them.

3. Your Move

Move two matches and make four squares, one of them larger than the other three.

4. Double Cross

The Equality Steamship Company is famous for the unfailing punctuality of its sailings. Every day at noon, Greenwich time, one of its liners leaves Southampton for New York and exactly at the same hour, also Greenwich time, another boat sails from New York to Southampton. The crossing, in either direction, takes seven days. Thus, whenever an Equality ship departs either from New York or from Southampton, another ship of the same line is just docking there, having arrived from the opposite direction. The eastbound and westbound liners ply the same course. If we board such a vessel at Southampton, how many Equality ships do we meet during our voyage to New York?

5. Shifting the Square

Starting with the position of the pieces at left, move them in such a way as to place the large square A in the position at right. It must, of course, be done without removing any of the pieces. *(Note:* This one, because of the many moves involved, cannot be done as a purely mental problem but should be constructed of cardboard or plywood, with a rectangular frame to insure that the player stays within bounds.)

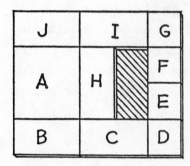
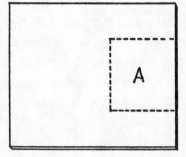

6. Secret Code

Leo Michael Linehan, a onetime cryptographer, describes a game that grows out of his interest in codes:

"One game that I often enjoy comes from recasting paragraphs in numerals according to the phone dial. Most people are already familiar with the layout:

2	3	4	5	6	7	8	9
A	D	G	J	M	P	T	W
B	E	H	K	N	R	U	X
C	F	I	L	O	S	V	Y

For Q and Z, I use 1, and 0 will serve for the spaces between words if you want to give yourself that advantage.

"I write my numerals down on a little pad and put it in my pocket. Then, in idle minutes, when I have safely forgotten the clear texts, I fish it out and try to reconstruct the words.

"This, of course, is not unlike deciphering a simple substitution cryptogram, except that a numeral may stand for any of three letters. It is by keeping these letters constantly in mind and revolving their plausible combinations that you can catch the words and phrases. (This is a great part of the intuitive activity of the cryptanalyst.)

"It has been a long time since I have had anything to do with serious cryptography. Sometimes this simple and sedate little exercise brings back a little of the absorption and *joie de faire* that I remember. But of course it is important to use texts that are trifling and uninteresting, the sort of thing you never notice and are unlikely to recall inadvertently in the middle of your game."

Try this one:
71827464084302472530470776252463304676774253028809 4280
36370467677425306326046062843628427084303477807832 6083
77350860276770843028526842022774330270727806304870 2274
60202665084280776833048092704676774253036702078326 0837
73508602767702698446406824053770843028526842

7. In Your Cups

Take a long piece of string and thread it through the handle of a teacup, exactly as shown, and tie the free ends to something. Can the cup be removed from the string without cutting it or undoing the knot?

8. The "Impossible" Problem

Just a glance at this problem is enough to reveal that it is impossible to move the block from the left-hand loop to the right-hand loop (without, of course, untying the rope), for the block is too big to fit through the hole in the bar. But *is* it really impossible?

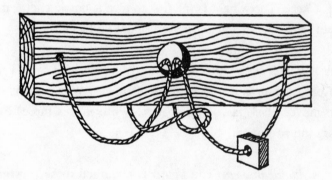

9. Chess Variations

Chess, absorbing as that game can be, can also be dull unless both players are fairly equally matched. Since it isn't always possible to find an opponent who is your equal, F. C. MacKnight has collected a number of chess variations that render normal knowledge of the game unnecessary or invalid. His descriptions follow:

a. *Replacement chess.* Men are not removed from the board. When captures are made the pieces are replaced on the board at a position chosen by the player who makes the capture. One must win by effectively cutting off the enemy king from his own forces.

b. *Progression chess.* Pawns do not "queen" but instead increase in power as they advance. The pawn on the fifth rank has the movement of the knight, on the sixth of a bishop, on the seventh of a rook, on the eighth of a queen. Moving backward, it loses its power the same way. Otherwise the game is played the same as standard chess.

c. *Check.* The winner is the first to give a simple check; mate is not necessary. The games are usually quite short.

d. *Addition chess.* Another variety of progressive chess where the progression is in the number of moves. White opens with one move, Black takes two moves. White makes three, Black four, and so forth.

e. *Cylindrical chess.* The board is imagined to be a cylinder with the edges adjoining, pieces slipping freely from one side of the board to the other. There are, in other words, no side edges.

f. *Secret arrangement of pieces.* A screen is placed at the midpoint of the board and each player arranges his men as he chooses.

26

10. Lineup

Draw four connected lines, without retracing your path, that pass through all the points:

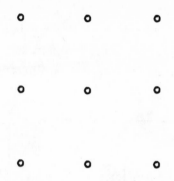

11. Super-Categories

The game of Categories is fairly well known, observes the same F. C. MacKnight, but not everyone knows that there are more intricate ways to play it:

"In the commonest form of Categories, one player chooses something and the rest try to find out what it is by asking questions which can be answered by yes or no. Sometimes it is called Animal-Vegetable-Mineral or Twenty Questions, but this is only an elementary variety played by those who cannot think of anything but objects easily placeable in space, and it isn't very good since immaterial things or abstractions cannot be rightly placed in any of these three categories. If you're working on something like the 'reflection of the full moon in the eye of the werewolf on a mountaintop of the Carpathians on Walpurgisnacht' (one I remember pleasurably solving), you don't get it in twenty questions. Or the 'concept of justice in the mind of Felix Frankfurter when he wrote his analysis of the Sacco-Vanzetti case.' Thus there should be no limit on the number of questions, or on the type of category. Variations of these games, which are numerous, usually involve some restriction, such as confining the play to places, people, cartoon characters, actors, etc."

12. Rugged Challenge

You have a 9×12-foot rug with an 8×1-foot hole in the middle. Cut the rug into two pieces (no more and no less) so that the two pieces can be sewn together to make a solid 10×10-foot rug.

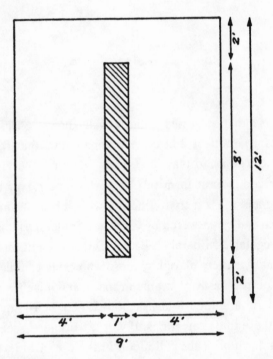

13. The Spider and the Fly

A 12×30-foot room has a 12-foot ceiling. In the middle of the end wall, a foot above the floor, is a spider. The spider wants to capture a fly in the middle of the opposite wall, one foot below the ceiling. What is the shortest path the spider can take?

14. Ups and Downs

A snail is at the bottom of a well 30 feet deep. It can crawl upward 3 feet in one day, but at night it slips back 2 feet. How long does it take the snail to crawl out of the well?

15. Jarring Experience

There are two jars of equal capacity. In the first jar there is one amoeba. In the second jar there are two amoebas. An amoeba can reproduce itself in three minutes. It takes the two amoebas in the second jar three hours to fill the jar to capacity. How long does it take the one amoeba in the first jar to fill that jar to capacity?

16. Time and Tide

A ship is at anchor. Over its side hangs a rope ladder with rungs a foot apart. The tide rises at the rate of 8 inches per hour. At the end of six hours how much of the rope ladder will remain above water, assuming that 8 feet were above water when the tide began to rise?

17. Case of the Clever Cook

A camp cook wants to measure four ounces of vinegar out of a jug, but he has only a five-ounce and a three-ounce container. How can he do it?

18. The Splintered Circle

What is the maximum number of parts into which a circle may be divided by drawing four straight lines?

19. Fast

A race driver drove around a 6-mile track at 140 mph for three miles, 168 mph for 1 1/2 miles, and 210 mph for 1 1/2 miles. What was his average speed for the entire 6 miles?

20. Catching Up

A truck travels 15 mph for the first half of the distance of a trip. How fast must it travel in the second half of the distance in order to average 30 mph for the total trip?

21. Sprouts

This game, played by two or more people, begins with a number of dots, preferably from three to ten. Taking turns, the players draw curves from dot to dot, each time putting a dot on the new line. The maximum permissible number of rays from each dot is three. The last one to draw a curve and dot wins. Here is how a game between two players, starting with five dots, might look:

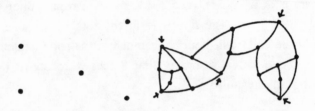

22. Cubes

Start off by drawing a cube (or, if you have them, use children's blocks). There is obviously only one way a single cube can be arranged—

so this is the end of the first series.

Next, do the same thing with two cubes. The results are identical—there is only one way to put them together:

With three cubes, there are two possible ways they may be arranged:

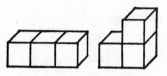

With four cubes there are seven ways:

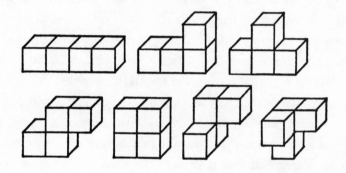

As for the rules, the only one is that cubes must abut face to face. The real puzzle is to find a formula for calculating the number of possible combinations for a given number of cubes. "Unfortunately," writes Alan E. Thompson, who invented the game, "I am not sure that there is such a rule. I think it probable that a computer would be needed once you got above the next two series." Anyone care to try?

23. Psychological Jujitsu

In this game all you need are unflinching nerves and an ability to think one jump ahead of your opponent when he's trying to do exactly the same thing to you. Required are the spade, club, and heart suits of a deck of cards. King counts 13, Queen 12, Jack 11, Ace 1, and all number cards count their number. Suits are of no consequence.

The object of the game is to win the greatest number of hearts. Player *A* takes the spade suit, player *B* the club suit. The hearts are shuffled, cut, and placed in a stack, face down, between the players.

Play begins with a heart being turned up from the top of the stack. Player *A* and player *B* each select one of their cards, placing it face down on the table. They then turn their cards over, and the player with the higher card wins the heart. This sequence is repeated for each of the thirteen tricks.

Each spade or club may be played only once, after which the cards are left face up, to remove all advantage of memory. If there is a tie on a play, the value of that card is split; the easiest way to accomplish that is to take the card out of the count. Forty-six heart points win.

As to possible strategies, there are three: Play to each heart at random; play a predetermined value for each heart; or determine your play as each heart turns up. Since both players start even, the winner wins by virtue of his ability to outthink his opponent. He wins, that is, by guessing what his opponent will, in effect, bid for a heart and then either trying to beat him by only one point or to lose by a lot.

Note: This is a superb game for children. Aside from being fun, it teaches them very quickly that life is complicated, unpredictable, and, all too often, terribly unfair.

32

24. Perspective

Kurt Nassau supplies a puzzle involving engineering drawings. In such drawings, the use of solid and dotted lines is most easily explained by an illustration—three views and a perspective drawing of the same object:

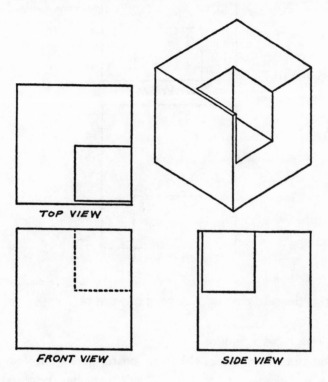

TOP VIEW

FRONT VIEW

SIDE VIEW

Now look at these two views of a different object:

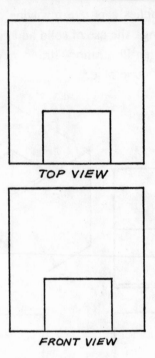

TOP VIEW

FRONT VIEW

What is the side view like? A perspective view?

25. Circles and a Square

Also from an engineer's drawing board, here's one I might never have figured out had not a kindly engineer friend taken pity on me and made me a small model of it. (It goes well on a key chain.) What is the shape depicted?

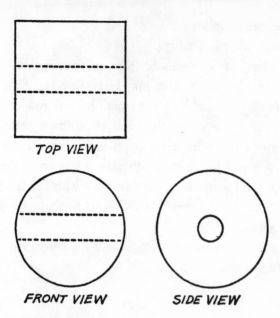

TOP VIEW

FRONT VIEW   SIDE VIEW

26. Matches in Rows

This one, to judge by the frequency with which it turns up in the archives of the superintelligent, is a special favorite. It appears to be simple, but the underlying principle eludes most people who try to analyze it.

The game is played with matches, which are placed in three rows. The top row has three matches, the second five matches, and the third seven matches. The object of the game is to make your opponent remove the last match.

The rules are as follows:

1. Players alternate moves.

2. Matches may be removed from only one row at a time.

3. Any number of matches may be removed by either player on his move, provided he takes from only one row at a time.

The game is played on the basis of "losing combinations." Each player tries to leave his opponent with such a combination. Once any of the losing combinations is given to your opponent he cannot win; losing combinations with the larger numbers of matches can simply be reduced to those made up of smaller numbers.

The game, as mentioned, starts with the combination 3-5-7. The losing combinations are:

> 2-5-7
> 3-4-7
> 3-5-6
> 1-4-5
> 1-2-3
> 1-1-1
> An even number in any two rows

If he knows these combinations, the person to move first can assure his victory simply by removing one match from any of the three rows. His opponent has lost before he has even begun.

III.

Words to the wise
(and from them, too)

For many of the superintelligent, word games are to be preferred above all other types of puzzles. One reason is that extremely bright people are, by definition, verbally adept people. Typically they have a way of noticing, delighting in, and remembering words that other people are likely to ignore or forget, and they are ordinarily very good at any challenge involving words. Though a very bright person may have seen words like *eyot* and *orrery* only once in his lifetime, he remembers what they mean when he encounters them again.* He knows, too, what six-letter word contains three y's** and what common English word has no rhyme.*** Beyond all that, he has a general verbal facility that makes playing word games and solving word puzzles as natural for him and as much fun as it is for Vida Blue to throw a baseball.

The fun comes in four main forms:

1. Tests and questions (like those above).

2. Standard games, such as Scrabble, Perquackey, crossword puzzles, and double-crostics.

---

* Eyot: an islet or small island. Orrery: a device for illustrating the motions of the planets.
** Syzygy.
*** Orange.

3. Made-up games, like Definitions (see below).

4. Just-messing-around games (also discussed below).

Let's look at some examples of each—and, in some cases, some inventive variations.

TESTS AND QUESTIONS

I have been collecting these, on odd scraps of paper, for years and have a good-sized collection ranging from the very simple to the quite difficult. Judge for yourself which of the following is which:

1. What eight-letter word contains only one vowel?

2. What word contains all five vowels in alphabetical order?

3. What word contains three sets of double letters in a row?

4. Punctuate the following so it makes sense: *John while James had had had had had had had had had had had a better effect on the teacher.*

What do the following words have in common: *deft, first, calmness, canopy, laughing, stupid, crabcake, hijack* (Puzzle 5). Jim Cochrane, commenting on first encountering this question, writes, "This one was bad for my ego. After I stared at it for five minutes or so, my wife, Carolyn, walked over, laughed, and informed me that it was obvious. I saw it several minutes later."

Finally, here is, in my opinion the world's most deceptively difficult spelling test—five perfectly ordinary English words that even many professional editors and writers fail to score a passing 60 per cent on. *(Stop!* Don't spoil it by looking; have someone read them to you.)

Inoculate

Iridescent

Rarefy

Kimono
Naphtha

As mentioned, these include such games as Scrabble, Perquackey, crossword puzzles, and double-crostics, all of them games with great appeal for many of the superintelligent. Characteristically, however, the superintelligent add special wrinkles of their own to increase the challenge. For example, in college I knew a kindly old government professor and Scrabble aficionado whose secret goal was to use words that were ever so slightly risqué. The high point of our series of matches, which went on over a number of years, was his triumphant spelling of *brassiere,* an accomplishment that not only earned him fifty extra points for using all seven of his tiles ("re" was already on the board) but also abundantly satisfied his special verbal idiosyncrasy.

Similarly, Perquackey, a game wonderfully suited to people of all ages from seven or eight upward, can be made into an equal contest for opponents of quite different abilities if the better player is simply required to use fewer of the lettered dice. When my ten-year-old son, John, and I play each other, he gains a slight advantage by using the three red dice, in addition to the seven black ones, while I must spell only with the black ones. Played that way, our games usually turn out to be remarkably close.

When it comes to crossword puzzles and double-crostics, I confess to an unaccountable blind spot. I am absolutely no good at either. In fact, I stand awed and humbled in the presence of a man like Henry Bate of Riverside, Connecticut, who on the morning commuter train likes to postpone doing the New York *Times* crossword puzzle until he has reached the 125th Street station. Then he races, usually without a flaw, through the whole puzzle in the nine or ten minutes between there and Grand Central. (During that time, of course, one attempts to engage Mr. Bate in conversation only at one's own peril.)

Still, I am open-minded enough to see that crosswords and double-crostics have proved pleasantly addictive to many, so I include here one of the more difficult of the former (Puzzle 6). It was composed by a fiendishly intelligent gentleman named N. A. S. Vincent, who is head of the Mathematics Department at Greenhill County Secondary School in Tenby, England. In offering it to me for use in this book, Mr. Vincent made the following confessional comment: "I used this crossword to round off a lesson on 'shape' with a General Studies sixth form. None of the class completed it, so I have provided some hints and answers. Some of the clues, I will agree, are contrived, but it gave an immense amount of pleasure and stimulated interest."

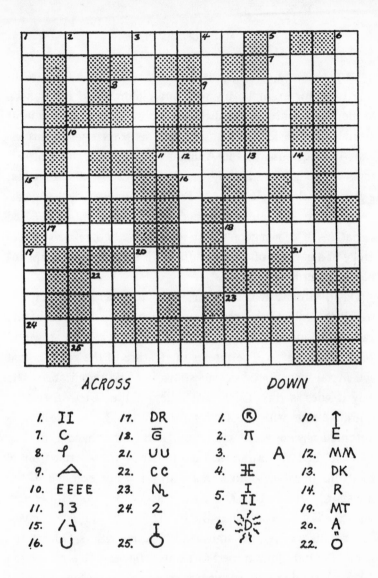

ACROSS

1. II	17. DR
7. C	18. $\overline{G}$
8. ⊹	21. UU
9. △	22. CC
10. EEEE	23. N₂
11.] 3	24. 2
15. /⅄	25. ⚲
16. U	

DOWN

1. ®	10. ↑E
2. π	12. MM
3. A	13. DK
4. ⅱ	14. R
5. I II	19. MT
6. ⚡D	20. A
	22. O

Well, don't say you weren't warned; I *said* Mr. Vincent was fiendish.

Of the making up of games there is no end. On long automobile trips, for example, my wife and children and I play such homemade games as Road Signs (see who can spell the most words with the letters on such signs as MASSACHUSETTS TURNPIKE—1/4 MILE AHEAD) and Animals (taking turns, think of animals whose names start with successive letters of the alphabet; *e.g.,* aardvark, bat, cat . . .). Practically everybody has composed games of their own at one time or another, or invented variations of known games, with the result that the precise genealogy of a game is often very difficult, if not downright impossible, to determine.

David Greene Kolodny, for example, describes a game in which the rule of the game is simply to state the rule of the game. The individual may ask questions that can be answered with a yes or a no. The interesting feature of the game is that the literal meaning of the questions is of no significance. The way it goes is this: If the last letter of the last word in the question ends with the letters from A to M, the question is automatically answered with a yes. On the other hand, if the last letter of the last word in the question ends with a letter from N to Z, the question is answered with a no. For example, if the question "Are you lying?" is asked, the answer is yes. If the next question is "Are you telling the truth?" the answer is again yes. The results can be quite amusing, Mr. Kolodny says. During one game, the questions turned to Dante's *Inferno.* One misguided player, assuming the answer was somehow to be found in that book, read the whole thing twice in an effort to solve the problem.

Another correspondent, Samuel A. Shaffe, confesses himself a partisan of a kind of cryptographic hide-and-seek. Two players each select a word (in this case, they agree to choose five-letter words with no repeated letters). Then, in turn, each player calls out a word and the other player tells how many of the letters in the mystery word are contained in that word. Mr. Shaffe says a sample game—an extremely simple one—might go something like this:

JOHN: My first word is *scene,* s-c-e-n-e. [Repeated letters, like the two *e*'s in *scene,* are not permitted in the secret words but are permitted in the calls.]

MARY: One letter. OK, I'll also say *scene.*

JOHN: You get two. I'll say *stems.*

MARY: You get a big round zero for *stems.* My next word is *steam.*

JOHN: *Steam* gives you four. Are you cheating or something? *Scant* is my word.

MARY: *Scant* gets you one. *Stage* is my next word.

JOHN: *Stage* gets you four again. *Slant,* s-l-a-n-t.

MARY: That's just one. *Least.*

JOHN: *Least* gives you five, but that's not the word. Well, it's hopeless now, but here goes: *tells.*

MARY: *Steal,* s-t-e-a-l. Is that your word?

JOHN: That's it, all right. You've got an LC in yours, but that's no help. What is it?

MARY: *Could,* you dummy. I win again!

Mr. Shaffe points out that the game can be made considerably more complicated by agreeing to choose longer words. Or, if a handicapping system is desired, one player might pick a four-letter word and the other, say, a six-letter word.

Finally, here is another one that has given me particular delight—a variant of the familiar childhood game called Ghost. In Ghost, you will remember, each player adds a letter until someone is forced to end the word. In this game, things are done a bit differently, though the object is still to avoid ending a word. Players alternate in starting with two letters, neither of which can be the first or last letters of the word. Subsequent players add one letter each, either at the beginning or the end. A typical game might go like this:

Player *A:* RD

Player *B:* RDR

Player *A:* ERDR

Player *B:* VERDR

Player *A:* OVERDR

Player *B:* (thinking of OVERDRAMATIC): OVERDRA

Player *A:* (avoiding the trap): OVERDRAF

Player *B:* OVERDRAFT (loses)

JUST-MESSING-AROUND GAMES

The true wordman can find pleasure practically anywhere anything has been written. He can, for example, have fun speculating on why some of the things in advertisements are written with such inventive ineptitude. I once found myself puzzling, for example, over the wording of an advertisement for sunglasses. The ad showed a boy wearing sunglasses. The headline read: "Look, Ma, I'm glancing at the world through [let's say] Ajax sunglasses." Thinking about the utter wrongness of that word "glancing," which no boy ever uttered in that context and no boy ever will, I thought I saw just what had happened: The copywriter, having written that "Look, Ma," didn't want to use "look" again, so groped for another word. His problem, poor fellow, was that "look" is just about the only right word to use there. What he should have done, of course, is change the first "look." A simple "Hey, Ma" would have done the trick.

Advertising, bless its busily creative heart, is full of such amusements.

Amusements of a different sort may be found in dictionaries, thesauruses, and books of quotations. I remember, for example, reading a magazine article some years ago in which the author, a man fascinated by the oddness of words, described himself as a kind of verbal zookeeper, a collector of strange specimens for no purpose other than to marvel at them. There are, I have since discovered, many such people, people who would rather track down and capture a curious word than the most exotic bird or butterfly.

Rita Schoch Sagers, for example, wonders about such questions as "What is the difference between flammable and inflammable?" And Ethel Wollman (who says "I am especially delighted with the kind of puzzle I can make up myself") offers a collection of definitions that she calls "Malapropossibles." Among them:

Symmetry: an Irish graveyard.

Kitty Hawk: a buzzard that eats cats.

Melancholic: what you get when you eat too much cantaloupe.

Mandate: a rendezvous with a fella.

Infatuate: to put on weight.

Gnu: what you've always known.

Sir Lancelot: a very busy medieval surgeon.

Olfactory: an ancient mill that smells.

Intent: an "at home" when you're on a camping trip.

Inspired by these examples, I came up with one of my own:

Questionable: what the police do when they interrogate a cow's husband.

See? It's easy. (If not always completely painless.) Your turn.

IV.

Those wonderful laws of logic (and how they can fool you every time)

The study of philosophy begins with logic, on the grounds that without clear thought the mind can't do much of anything. At the outset, therefore, students of philosophy learn such useful principles as the fact that a thing cannot simultaneously be A and not A, that syllogisms must follow a certain pattern in order to be valid, and that to find fault with a person is not the same as finding fault with his argument. After a brief immersion in this sort of thing, the student may be forgiven if he begins to think he has acquired some quite potent instruments for validating truth and sniffing out error. And of course he has—provided other people play the game by the rules and agree not to use *ad hominem* arguments, not to be deliberately misleading (40 per cent more effective than *what?),* not to sulk, not to pound fists and shoes on the table, and not to bully each other with patriotic slogans and full-page ads in *Life.* The trouble, as we all know, is that such agreements never stay in effect for long. No, the fact is that we often set out *deliberately* to mislead each other, with results familiar to us all.

This chapter consists of some of the pleasanter, more harmless examples of such attempts to mislead, or at least to force the victim to use something beyond mere plodding, dogged logic. For it will be seen at once that these puzzles have one thing in common: Not a single one of them will yield up its secret to mere diligence or persistence; at least a pinch of brilliance must be thrown in. Every one of them, in other words, requires some leap of logic that must sometimes be merely clever and sometimes dazzlingly brilliant. But it must always be considerably more than all but the superintelligent (and perhaps a few of their closest intellectual kin) can muster.

1. Warmup

This is an old one but still a good one. (Max Batchelder, a member of Mensa and a puzzle enthusiast, calls it "my all-time favorite.") It takes many different forms, as virtually all the old favorites among puzzles do; here it is as Mr. Batchelder gives it:

"A hunter arose early, ate breakfast, and headed south. Half a mile from camp he tripped and skinned his nose. He picked himself up, cursing, and continued south. Half a mile farther along, he spotted a bear. Drawing a bead, he pulled the trigger, but the safety was on. The bear saw him and headed east at top speed. Half a mile later the hunter caught up, fired, but only wounded the beast, which limped on toward the east. The hunter followed and half a mile later caught and killed the bear. Pleased, the hunter walked the mile north back to his camp to find it had been ransacked by a second bear.

"What color was the bear that tore up his camp?"

The clues are all there.

2. Cutting Up

A carpenter wants to cut a cube of wood into 27 equal cubes. It is obvious that he can accomplish this with six cuts:

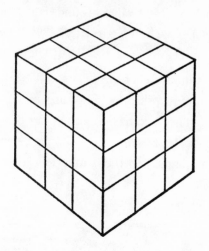

Is there any procedure that would require fewer than six cuts? If there is, describe it. If there isn't, explain why not.

3. Taking Sides

Given: Four pieces of cardboard. You are told that each one is either red or green on one side, and that each one has either a circle or a square on the other side. They appear on the table as follows:

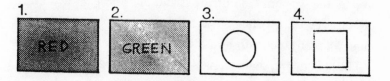

Which ones must you pick up and turn over in order to have sufficient information to answer the question: Does every red one have a square on its other side?

4. No Peeking

Three boxes are labeled "Apples," "Oranges," and "Apples and Oranges." Each label is incorrect. You may select only one fruit from one box. (No feeling around or peeking permitted.) How can you label each box correctly?

5. Case of the Counterfeit Coin

You have twelve identical-looking coins, one of which is counterfeit. The counterfeit coin is either heavier or lighter than the rest. The only scale available is a simple balance. Using the scale only three times, find the counterfeit coin.

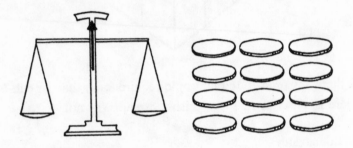

6. True or False?

A missionary visits an island where two tribes live. One tribe always tells the truth. The other always lies. The truth tellers live on the western side of the island and the liars live on the eastern side of the island. The missionary's problem is to determine who tells the truth by asking one native only one question.

The missionary, seeing a native walking in the distance, asks a nearby native: "Go ask that native in the distance which side of the island he lives on." When the messenger returns he answers: "He says he lives on the western side of the island." Is the messenger a truth teller or a liar? How can you be sure?

7. More Natives

In the South Pacific, so the story goes, white people get sunburned to a brown color that is identical to the native islanders' color. There is only one way to tell them apart: by what they say. Islanders always lie. Non-islanders always tell the truth.

A visitor is paddling a canoe up to the beach of an island when he sees three people, all the same brown color. He asks, "Are you white people burned brown or are you islanders?" The first one calls out something that is lost in the sound of the surf, so the man in the canoe again shouts, "Are you islanders or sunburned white people?"

This time the second man on the beach calls back, saying, "The first person who answered said he is a white man, and he *is* a white man, and so am I." The third person on the beach called out, "The first two people here on the beach are islanders and I am a white man burned brown."

From what they have said, tell what each man really is.

8. Dog Days

This one is tough but can be solved by a strict application of logic (provided you've got a goodly amount of serendipity to go along with it). It comes from Irving Hale, who describes it this way:

"This 'cross-number puzzle' was given to me by a secretary at the bank where I formerly was employed. I don't know where she got it but it is obviously English and around thirty years old. It is a marvelous problem. Solving it requires a well-balanced combination of logic, calculation, and trial-and-error. The numbers are so interlocked that practically every one of them must be employed in reaching the final entry (2 down.)

"The puzzle concerns a farm that has been in the Dunk family for some years. A part of the farm is a rectangular piece of ground known as Dog's Mead. Additional background information: The year is 1939; 4840 square yards = one acre; 4 roods = one acre."

Across

1. Area in square yards of Dog's Mead
5. Age of Martha, Father Dunk's aunt
6. Difference in yards between length and breadth of Dog's Mead
7. Number of roods in Dog's Mead times 8 down
8. The year the Dunks acquired Dog's Mead
10. Father Dunk's age
11. Year of Mary's birth
14. Perimeter in yards of Dog's Mead
15. Cube of Father Dunk's walking speed in mph
16. 15 across minus 9 down

Down

1. Value in shillings per rood of Dog's Mead
2. Square of the age of Father Dunk's mother-in-law
3. Age of Mary, Father Dunk's other daughter
4. Value in pounds of Dog's Mead
6. Age of Ted, Father Dunk's son, who is twice the age of his sister Mary in 1945
7. Square of the breadth of Dog's Mead
8. Time in minutes it takes Father Dunk to walk 1$1/3$ times around Dog's Mead
9. The number which, multiplied by 10 across, gives 10 down
10. See 9 down
12. Addition of the digits of 10 down plus 1
13. Number of years Dog's Mead has been in the Dunk family

9. Theirs to Reason Why

The same Easy Sloman mentioned in Chapter 1 has sent me his version of one of the most popular of all logic puzzles. It is, in fact, so popular and—to true aficionados—so common that at least one friend has urged me not to mention it again for fear of driving readers away. I think it's a wonderful puzzle, though, no matter how familiar, so here it is:

Three intelligent men, applying for a job, seem equal in all pertinent attributes, so the prospective employer, also an intelligent man, sets a simple problem for them. The job, he says, will go to the first applicant to solve it. A mark is placed on each man's forehead. The three are told that each has either a black mark or a white mark, and each is to raise his hand if he sees a black mark on the forehead of either of the other two. The first one to tell what color he has and how he arrived at his answer will get the job. Each man raised his hand, and after a few

53

seconds one man comes up with the answer. What color was his mark, and how did he figure it out?

10. Variation

If you think *that* one is hard, consider the same problem with not just three but *four* job applicants. All four are told that they are exceptionally intelligent. They are, in fact, all familiar with the three-person puzzle (above), and each knows that the other three are familiar with it, too. They are asked two questions: Anyone who can see two black marks is to stand up; and anyone who knows the color of the mark on his own forehead is to raise his hand. All four men stand up. Then, after a few minutes, one of them raises his hand and correctly announces the color of his mark. What was it and how did he know?

11. Love Story

Four men and four women are shipwrecked on a desert island. Eventually each one falls in love with one other, and is himself loved by one person. John falls in love with a girl who is, unfortunately, in love with Jim. Arthur loves a girl who loves the man who loves Ellen. Mary is loved by the man who is loved by the girl who is loved by Bruce. Gloria hates Bruce and is hated by the man whom Hazel loves. Who loves Arthur?

12. Zoo Story

MAN: How many birds and how many beasts do you have in your zoo?

ZOOKEEPER: There are 30 heads and 100 feet.

MAN: I can't tell from *that.*

ZOOKEEPER: Oh, yes you can!

Can *you?*

54

13. Batter Up!

Andy dislikes the catcher. Ed's sister is engaged to the second baseman. The center fielder is taller than the right fielder. Harry and the third baseman live in the same building. Paul and Allen each won $20 from the pitcher at pinochle. Ed and the outfielders play poker during their free time. The pitcher's wife is the third baseman's sister. The pitcher, catcher, and infielders except Allen, Harry, and Andy, are shorter than Sam. Paul, Andy, and the shortstop lost $50 each at the racetrack. Paul, Harry, Bill, and the catcher took a trouncing from the second baseman at pool. Sam is involved in a divorce suit. The catcher and the third baseman each have two children. Ed, Paul, Jerry, the right fielder, and the center fielder are bachelors. The others are married. The shortstop, the third baseman, and Bill each cleaned up $100 betting on the fight. One of the outfielders is either Mike or Andy. Jerry is taller than Bill. Mike is shorter than Bill. Each of them is heavier than the third baseman.

Using these facts, determine the names of the men playing the various positions on the baseball team.

14. Bang

Two automobiles are approaching each other at a constant velocity of 60 mph. When the autos are two miles apart, a very fast fly leaves the front bumper of one of the autos and travels toward the other at a speed of 120 mph. Upon reaching that auto, the fly immediately reverses direction. This continues until the autos collide (or, to make it less gory, let's say narrowly *miss* colliding). How far did the fly travel?

15. Checkmate

A standard chessboard is truncated by removing two corner squares diagonally opposite each other. Can thirty-one dominoes, each able to cover two adjacent squares, be used to cover all sixty-two squares of the truncated chessboard? If so, how? If not, why not?

16. Question

A traveler comes to a fork in the road and does not know which way to go to reach his destination. There are two men at the fork, one of whom always lies while the other always tells the truth. The traveler doesn't know which is which. He may ask one of the men only one question to find his way. What is his question and which man does he ask?

17. Probabilities

You have 10 gray socks and 20 blue socks in your bureau drawer. If you reach into it in the dark, how many socks must you take out to be sure of having a pair that matches?

V.

The fine, frustrating art of numbermanship

If you like puzzles, there is no more pleasant or effective way to while away, say, a long airplane trip than to take along two or three tough, intricate problems and some scratch paper. I did just that not long ago on a flight from New York to Los Angeles and in the process discovered what promptly became my all-time favorite mathematical puzzle. It seems to me to demand just the right combination of logic, intuition, and trial-and-error. Though essentially simple, it is also tricky in its way, each piece of the solution dovetailing with the next like the parts of a Chinese puzzle. There are thousands of mathematical problems—any good library contains a surprising number of books on the subject—but for my money there can never be too many like this one:

1. Multiplying by 4
Supply a digit for each letter so that the equation is correct. There is only one set of digits that will work. A given letter always represents the same digit:

$$
\begin{array}{ccccc}
A & B & C & D & E \\
  &   &   & \times & 4 \\
\hline
E & D & C & B & A \\
\end{array}
$$

57

2. Compound Interest

And here's an elegant little addition problem:

```
    S  E  N  D
+   M  O  R  E
───────────────
 M  O  N  E  Y
```

3. Lost and Found

In the rearranged triangle (right), where does the extra square come from?

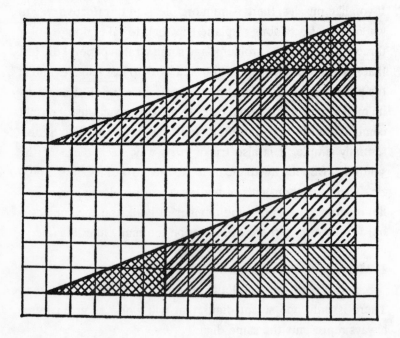

Andrew F. Bender calls this puzzle "the most intriguing I have ever encountered." He says it has "stumped more people than ony other puzzle I know."

4. Missing Number

Supply the missing number in the following sequence:

10
11
12
13
14
15
16
17
20
22
24
31
100
?
10000
1111111111111111

5. Two Buckets

One bucket contains a gallon of water, another a gallon of alcohol. A cup of alcohol from the second bucket is poured into the bucket of water. A cup of the resulting mixture is then poured back into the bucket of alcohol. Is there:

(a) More water in the alcohol than alcohol in the water;

(b) More alcohol in the water than water in the alcohol;

(c) The same amount of water in the alcohol as alcohol in the water?

6. Homeward Bound

Each day a man's wife meets him at the railroad station and drives him home. One day he arrives at the station an hour early and begins to walk home along the road his wife always takes. She meets him en route and takes him the rest of the way home. Had he waited at the station, she would have picked him up exactly on time. As it turned out, he reached his home twenty minutes early. How long did the man walk?

7. Weighty Problem

If you have a balance scale, what is the minimum number of weights that can be used to weigh any number of pounds from one to forty? What are the weights?

8. And now, in ring one . . .

A circus performance is witnessed by 120 people who have paid a total of $120. The men paid $5, the women $2, and the children 10¢ each. How many of each went to the circus?

9. Monkey Business

A rope over the top of a fence has the same length on each side. It weighs one third of a pound per foot. On one end hangs a monkey holding a banana, and on the other end a weight equal to the weight of the monkey. The banana weighs two ounces per inch. The rope is as long (in feet) as the age of the monkey (in years), and the weight of the monkey (in ounces) is the same as the age of the monkey's mother. The combined ages of the monkey and its mother are thirty years. One half the weight of the monkey, plus the weight of the banana, is one fourth as much as the weight of the weight and the weight of the rope. The monkey's mother is half as old as the monkey will be when it is three times as old as its mother was when she was half

60

as old as the monkey will be when it is as old as its mother will be when she is four times as old as the monkey was when it was twice as old as its mother was when she was one third as old as the monkey was when it was as old as its mother was when she was three times as old as the monkey was when it was one fourth as old as it is now. How long is the banana?

10. Bridge into Troubled Waters

A genius came to a narrow railroad bridge and began to run across it. He had crossed three eighths of the distance when a whistle behind him warned of an approaching train. Being a genius, he instantly evaluated his alternatives. If he were to run back to the beginning of the bridge at his speed of 10 mph, he would leave the bridge at precisely the moment the train entered it. If he kept on running to the end of the bridge, the train would reach him just as he left the bridge. At what speed was the train moving?

11. Stringing Along

A man buys a string 25,000 miles long and sets out to stretch it around the circumference of the earth. When he reaches his starting point, he discovers that the string is in fact 25,000 miles and one yard long. Rather than cut the string, he decides to tie the ends together and distribute the extra 36 inches evenly around the entire circumference. How far does the string stand out from the earth because of the extra yard? (Disregard the length of string used to tie the knot.)

12. Equations That Changed the World

Nicaragua, a country that must be a mathematician's paradise, not long ago issued ten postage stamps bearing LAS 10 FORMULAS MATEMATICAS QUE CAMBIARON LA FAZ DE LA TERRA

(The 10 mathematical formulas that changed the face of the world). How many of them can you identify?

(a) $1+1=2$

(b) $f=\dfrac{Gm_1m_2}{r^2}$

(c) $E=mc^2$

(d) $e^{\ln N}=N$

(e) $A^2+B^2=C^2$

(f) $S=k \log W$

(g) $V=V_e \ln\dfrac{m_0}{m_1}$

(h) $\lambda=h/mv$

(i) $V^2E=\dfrac{Ku}{c^2}\dfrac{\delta^2E}{\delta t^2}$

(j) $F_1x_1=F_2X_2$

13. $3+3=4$

Here's one that clearly calls for the "sideways approach" that was mentioned earlier, for a moment's reflection will reveal that it cannot be done in any ordinary way. The problem is simply to arrange four pennies so that there are two straight lines with three pennies on each line.

If you can do that one in five minutes or less, then you've thoroughly caught on to the mental phenomena that this book is all about. (Those phenomena are discussed in more specific detail in the following chapter.)

VI.

The superintelligent: how they got that way and how they stay that way

In the preceding pages we've been talking a great deal about human intelligence. We've been making some observations about how it works, what it can accomplish and what, if a person doesn't have enough of it, it can't accomplish. This whole book is, in fact, built on the premises that 1) there is indeed something properly identifiable as intelligence and that 2) some people have more of it—in some cases a lot more of it—than others.

But now, in the face of all that, it is also necessary to admit that no one really knows what intelligence is, or even whether there is any objective quality or set of qualities that conforms to our notion of what constitutes intelligence. "How far these 'qualities' represent some objective reality in the personality and how far they are constructs of the human mind in relation to the behavior of the person we are unable to judge," writes Victor Serebriakoff.

In short, no one knows exactly what intelligence is (the only thing we're absolutely certain intelligence tests do is measure what intelligence tests measure), yet we all agree, somehow, that there is such a thing as intelligence. We are all likely to agree, too, that it is parceled out quite unequally among the human species.

Furthermore, it has been shown that I.Q.—which is nothing more than intelligence in relation to an individual's chronological age—has certain typical characteristics. Researchers have discovered, for example, that intelligence normally stops increasing at the beginning of adolescence (except in the case of certain very bright people whose intelligence may continue developing until eighteen or so). This is not to say, however, that the ability to *use* one's intelligence cannot be improved well beyond that time. In fact, if a reader has been diligent enough to work his way this far into this book, he has probably discovered a number of mental techniques that had not previously been in his armamentarium. He is, it is true, fundamentally no more intelligent, but he may be able to *do* more with his intelligence. For that reason his I.Q.—which, remember, is by definition simply what an I.Q. test measures—may actually be slightly higher. And to anyone who watches him unerringly solve an unfamiliar problem he will certainly *look* more intelligent.

There is, therefore, something we can do about improving the *use* of intelligence, though there is considerable room for debate over just how much we can do. (One recent estimate is that 80 per cent of intelligence is nature, only 20 per cent nurture.) One way to improve one's ability to use one's mind is simply to see how very bright people use theirs. Let's look closely at a few of the puzzles that appear in this book with an eye to finding out what the superintelligent do that's different from what ordinary people do.

64

1. *The OTTFFSS series problem (Chapter I, Question 1).* The solver first tries the most obvious routes—the intervals between the letters, the pattern of single and double letters, and so forth—but finds no clues there. Finally he begins to suspect ɩnat he needs to search for an entirely different kind of solution. But what kind? He thinks, perhaps, of such things as the sounds of the letters and their shapes. Nothing there. Finally, still looking for something he now knows must be very different from the more obvious solutions, he asks himself: Do the letters *stand* for something? Persistence alone will now bring its reward, and eventually a thought occurs to him: *O*ne, *T*wo, *T*hree . . . !

The key here, I think, is the puzzler's confidence that he has thoroughly examined each possible level of solution before discarding it. As one level proves fruitless, he feels justified in turning his full attention to the next possibility. He does not linger over apparently lost causes.

2. *The four squares problem (II, 3).* Anyone trying to solve this one, whether or not he is extraordinarily bright, will quickly see that it is impossible to do what the problem seems at first glance to call for—that is, to make four identical squares out of five by moving just two matches. Trial and error will reveal that much within a minute or two. While the ordinary person is likely to continue trying to solve it in those terms, the bright person looks for an escape route. What might such a route be? Can the problem be solved by using the third dimension? No, for that would require more than just two matches. Finally it occurs to him that all the squares need not be the same size. With that realization he is suddenly very close to the answer (and to the realization that there is nothing in the problem that says one

65

square can't be inside another). The key question the puzzler needs to ask himself is: "What assumptions about the conditions of the problem am I making that I need not make?" Once he has broken free of two unnecessary assumptions he has the problem solved.

3. *The nine dots problem (II, 10).* Who said the lines had to stay inside the boundaries of the dots? The intelligent person tries, as we saw above, not to impose unnecessary restrictions on his mind.

4. *The apples and oranges puzzle (IV, 4).* Both the ordinary person and the bright person see one thing clearly right away: that if, for example, a fruit is picked from the box marked "Apples," it can be either an apple or an orange and will therefore tell nothing about whether the box should be marked "Oranges" or "Apples and Oranges." Since the same is true if a fruit is picked from the box marked "Oranges," it is tempting to conclude that the same will also be true of the third box, "Apples and Oranges." But the bright person does not take that supposition for granted. Instead, he goes ahead and tries it. Suppose, he thinks, I pick a fruit from "Apples and Oranges" and it turns out to be an orange—then what do I know about what's in that box? Well, for one thing, since we have been told that all the boxes are wrongly labeled, we know that it is not "Apples and Oranges." Therefore it must be oranges. Then the remaining boxes contain apples and apples and oranges. But which contains which? Simple. Remember once again that the boxes are all mislabeled. Simply switch the two remaining labels and the problem is solved. The bright person has succeeded because he does not assume the problem cannot be solved sim-

ply because it cannot be solved in one way or even two ways he has tried. He tries every alternative.

5. *The three applicants problem (IV, 9)*. This is another of those puzzles that at first glance looks impossible. After all, it appears that the only thing any of the applicants can know is that at least one black mark is visible, and clearly the problem can't be solved on the basis of that piece of information alone. Therefore something else must also be known. But what? Here is where the really intelligent person, rather than feeling defeated, moves into high gear, eventually realizing that he also knows something of the reasoning process that must be going on in the applicants—and that the solution may lie in that fact. Since all three applicants raised their hands, he reasons, there were two possibilities: two black and a white or three black. If, therefore, there were a white mark on any forehead, two men would see one black and one white and would instantly deduce that the third mark must be black. Since this instant solution did not occur, each of the three men saw two black marks. Therefore all were black, including the mark of the successful applicant.

6. *The two cars problem (IV, 14)*. This is a straightforward calculus problem, but one that is complicated enough to be beyond the ability of most merely amateur mathematicians. In cases like this, very bright people realize, it is usually worthwhile to look closely and see if there may be some easy shortcut to a solution. In this case, there is. The secret lies in the fact that the total time the two cars travel is one minute. Since the fly goes at 120 miles per hour (and reverses direction *immediately*), he will go two miles during that time, calculus or no calculus. The ease

of the solution is enough to elicit a groan from any earnest calculus student.

7. *The chessboard problem (IV, 15).* Practically everyone attacks this one in precisely the wrong way—by trial and error. Using a chessboard, or perhaps just a pencil and paper, one tries repeatedly to cover the sixty-two squares with the thirty-two dominoes. No success. It is at this point, I think, that the two principal types of minds begin to diverge. The very intelligent mind, in its purposeful way, is likely to form a hypothesis— that the dominoes can't cover the squares. For if that hypothesis is correct, he is one big step ahead of his less bright competitors. (If, of course, the hypothesis is not correct, he is off on a wild goose chase, but the alternative is simply to keep trying different ways of putting dominoes on squares.) All right, then, he asks, just *why* won't it work? He tries numbering the lines of squares; that course yields nothing worthwhile. But perhaps he does notice that a given square, if its assigned number is odd, must always combine with an even square. From there it is only a slight jump to the realization that each square has its own color and that a black square must always combine with a white. Since the two missing squares are the same color—eureka!—at the end there will always be two squares left over.

8. *The fork in the road problem (IV, 16).* At first it appears that there is no way, with only one question, to find out (a) if the person asked is the liar or the truth teller and (b) if his fork in the road is the right one or the wrong one. Won't the one question be used up in finding out whether the man is telling the truth or lying, leaving no way to find out the second part of the problem? Apparently so—until it occurs to the puzzler that it may somehow be possible to ask a question whose answer will

not depend on which person is asked. Once he is on that trail, the idea of the double falsehood (or double truth, as the case may be) comes easily and he sees that the question to ask is: "If I were to ask you if this is the way I should go, would you say yes?" He also sees that it doesn't matter which man he asks.

9. *The multiplied letters (V, 1).* The peculiar beauty of this one is that it can be done in an elegantly logical way. It is worth going through step by step, as an illustration of how an apparently difficult problem yields to a certain sort of mind:

a. The puzzler realizes that, since A multiplied by 4 yields only a one-digit answer, it must be either 1 or 2.

b. Since E × 4 must yield an even number, A must be 2.

c. Since the only numbers that, when multiplied by 4, yield a figure ending with 2, are 3 and 8, E must be either 3 or 8.

d. Since A × 4 cannot be 13—*i.e.,* cannot be a two-digit number—it must be 8. Therefore E is 8.

e. Since a 3 is carried over to D in the top line, it must also be added to D in the answer. We can see that B × 4 must yield a one-digit number. That means that B must be either a 1 or a 2. If it is a 2, then with the 3 added to it, D would be 11—impossible. So B must be 1.

f. Now consider D. The question here is simple: What number, when multiplied by 4 and enlarged by the carried 3, will yield a number ending in 1? Two numbers fill the bill: 2 and 7. Since we already know that B is 1, the missing number must be 7.

g. The B in the top line must have a carried 3 added to it in order to yield 7 in the answer, so C, when its carried 3 is added to it, must be at least 30. The only numbers that will work, therefore, are 7, 8 or 9. A little experimentation shows that 9 is the missing number.

10. *The four coins puzzle (V, 13)*. A few moments' study shows that this one can't be done in two dimensions, as we assume at first it must be done. But who said it *has* to be done in two dimensions? The true puzzler, instead of trying an approach that is clearly impossible, gropes for some loophole and, with luck, quickly finds it in the third dimension. Then all he needs to do is arrange three coins in a triangle and put the fourth on top of one of them. (I will confess that this has a certain willful trickiness that many puzzlers, myself included, find distasteful. Many others, on the other hand, like puzzles that contain a certain amount of verbal trickery. *De gustibus non disputandum est.)*

These, then, are a few of the ways very nimble-witted people solve problems. Their most telling mental characteristic seems to be a restless agility that is willing to abandon an apparently fruitless approach and try another one, no matter how improbable it looks at first. (Isn't it too bad more statesmen don't think that way, too?) It can all be reduced, really, to one simple formula: *Don't give up.*

Everybody in class clear on that lesson? Final examinations follow.

VII.

So you think you're pretty bright? (Well, maybe you are.)

In the past ten years Mensa, the high I.Q. society, has tested some 100,000 people to determine just where they rank in intelligence. To do this, the organization has developed special tests that are more challenging, more interesting, and—let's be candid about it—very often more maddeningly impenetrable than ordinary intelligence tests. The following test, modeled on those actually used by Mensa, was specially devised for this book by Mensa's research director and guru-in-residence, Max L. Fogel, Ph.D. It is, he says with an almost straight face, "not particularly tough, although some of the questions may be confusing at first." Well, don't let a little confusion discourage you; in this league, that's supposed to be part of the fun.

1. If seven belly dancers can lose a total of 20 pounds in eight hours of dancing, how many more belly dancers would be needed to lose a total of 20 pounds in only four hours of dancing provided the new dancers shed weight only half as fast as the original seven?

    (a) 7   *(b)* 21   *(c)* 27   *(d)* 14   *(e)* 12

2. Some Mensa members are geniuses. All geniuses have some human virtues as redeeming qualities. Therefore:

(a) Mensa members all have some virtue.

(b) All geniuses are quality Mensa members.

(c) Some Mensa members have redeeming qualities.

3. $\sqrt{I}$ is to C^2 as B^3 is to D times _____.

(a) B   *(b)* C   *(c)* D   *(d)* E   *(e)* F

4. Fill in the blank spaces by selecting one of the four lettered alternatives.

Marlon Brando	Ingrid Bergman	Ingmar Bergman	(1)	Igor Stravinsky
Sophia Loren	(2)	Pablo Picasso	Charles Ives	Richard Burton
Luis Bunuel	Jackson Pollock	Sergei Prokofiev	(3)	(4)

(a) (1) Paul Klee; (2) Rudolph Nureyev: (3) Vivien Leigh; (4) Joan Miro

(b) (1) Georges Braque; (2) Federico Fellini; (3) Dustin Hoffman; (4) Elizabeth Taylor

(c) (1) Jon Voight; (2) Alfred Hitchcock; (3) Leontyne Price; (4) Richard Tucker

(d) (1) Aaron Copland; (2) Paul Cezanne; (3) Helen Hayes; (4) John Wayne

5. "A stream cannot rise higher than its source" means:

(a) You decline after achieving your highest level.

(b) Streams of knowledge don't come from high sources.

(c) Your stream of consciousness is highly resourceful.

(d) Your stream of achievement is limited by your background.

(e) Gravitational factors prevent water from running uphill.

6. Which one does not belong?

(a) dada *(b)* abstract expressionist *(c)* cubist *(d)* dodecaphonic *(e)* pointillist

7. Consider the series of diagrams on the top line. Which diagram on the bottom line comes next in the series?

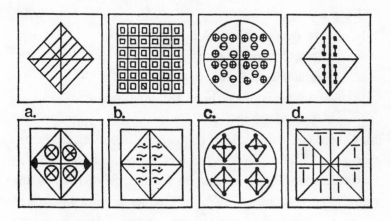

8. Which one does not belong?

(a) chess *(b)* bridge *(c)* go *(d)* Mah-Jongg *(e)* backgammon

9. "The used key is always bright" means:

(a) Keep on the scene in order to stay with it.

(b) If you use a test key you will appear bright.

(c) New devices often don't work very well.

(d) Old ideas are the best.

10. Complete the series: 2-4; 6-18; _____.

    (a) 8-24   *(b)* 8-32   *(c)* 10-40   *(d)* 20-60   *(e)* 21-84

11. "A rolling stone gathers no moss" means:

    (a) None of the Rolling Stones smoke marijuana.

    (b) Shifting stones around in a rock garden prevents weeds.

    (c) Rock collections don't appreciate in value with time.

    (d) Stay in your groove to do your thing.

12. All readers of this book greatly love puzzles. Some readers of this book are famous. Some famous people are great lovers. Therefore:

    (a) All readers of this book become famous.

    (b) All great lovers are puzzling.

    (c) Some famous people love puzzles.

    (d) Some readers of this book are great lovers.

13. Greens are better farklers (farkleberry collectors, of course) than most Purples. However, in farkling competition in which the income of Greens is equal to the income of Purples, the matches are standoffs. Farkling ability has been demonstrated by independent researchers to have a possible connection with diet. The Greens have more money than the Purples and can afford better farkling instruction. The most promising approach to equalization of farkling ability in the two groups would probably be to:

    (a) Provide farkling ability dietary ingredients to the Purples.

    (b) Equalize the wealth by giving enough Green money to Purples.

    (c) Make sure the Purples have sufficient nourishment for good health.

(d) Obtain better farkling teachers and equipment for the Purples.

14. C, G, Q are to F, V, R as T, X, H are to:

(a) V, L, G   *(b)* B, F, Y   *(c)* W, M, I   *(d)* N, Z, D

15. "The good is the enemy of the best" means:

(a) If you're good you'll best your enemy.

(b) Be good to your best enemy.

(c) Don't accept less than your best.

(d) The good struggles against the best.

16. Complete the series:

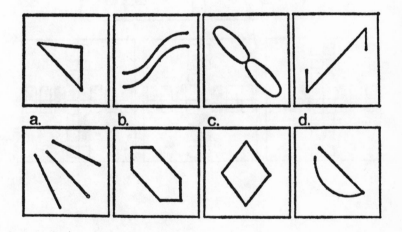

a.   b.   c.   d.

17. Grsmr kxcgob sc mybbomd?

(a) Ylfsyecvi xyd drsc yxo.

(b) Pybqod sd.

(c) Iye kbo k qyyn qeoccob.

(d) Kxydrob sxknoaekdo kddowzd.

18. Complete the series:

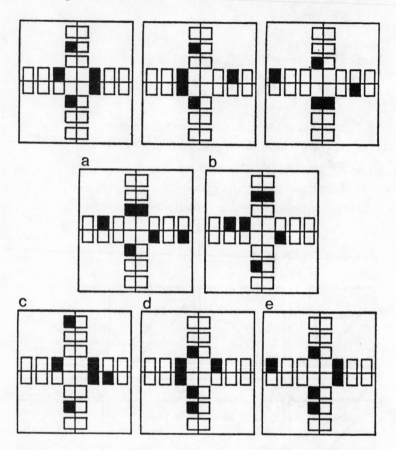

The helpers

Frederick B. Artz of Oberlin, Ohio, a man with as facile and inventive a mind as I will ever know, once observed: "You don't *cook* hash; you *accumulate* it." And so it is with this book. It is not so much a written book as an accumulated one, and it could not have been accumulated without the help of a great many selflessly brilliant people who took time to correspond with me and talk with me about puzzles that are particular favorites of theirs, as well as about questions of human intelligence in general. Among those who, for one reason or another, have earned my special thanks are:

R. C. Allais, Randolph W. Banner, Max Batchelder, Henry Bate, S. Bayne, Andrew F. Bender, Richard Boeth, Roger Brewis, Betty Burney, Jim Cochrane, Roger Crabtree, Madeline B. Cuthbertson, Crazy Eddie Epstein, H. de Grote, the late P. T. Fenn, Jr., Max L. Fogel, Michael J. H. Gerrard, I. J. Good, Bostock Hackett III, Irving Hale, E. C. Hanford, Ellis Hardy, Alice Kasman, David Greene Kolodny, Norris F. Krueger, Leo Michael Linehan, Christina M. Lyon, James MacFadyen, F. C. MacKnight, James J. Madigan, Arthur A. Merrill, Kurt Nassau, Norbert A. Nizze, Grose Perla, John Power, Rita Schoch Sagers, Vern Schuman, Victor Serebriakoff, Samuel A. Shaffe, Easy Sloman, Joseph Smrcka, Alan E. Thompson, James F. Vance, N. A. S. Vincent, Joe Wagner, Donn Wallace, Ernest Wedge, Nelson Winget, Ethel Wollman and whoever hung the rope trick on the maple tree at the Seton Boy Scout Reservation.

Answers to puzzles

1. The next letter in the sequence O T T F F S S is E. The letters are the initial letters of *O*ne, *T*wo, *T*hree. . . . but you know the rest.

2. There are 20 9's from 1 to 100. Or did you forget 90, 91, 92, 93 . . . etc.?

3. Since the 8-inch diagonal is the same length as the circle's radius, the answer is 8 inches.

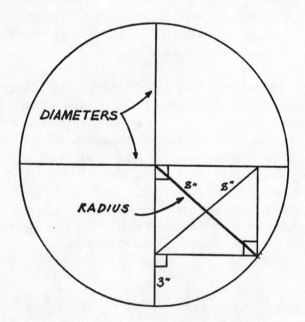

CHAPTER II

1. *(a)*

$$\frac{\text{XXII}}{\text{VII}} = \text{TT}$$

(b)

$$\text{VT} = \text{I}$$

2.

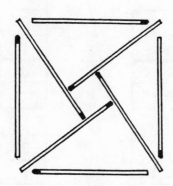

3.

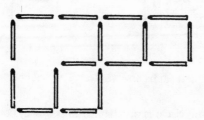

4. The Equality Steamship Company operates sixteen ships and we pass all of them—except, of course, our own.

5.

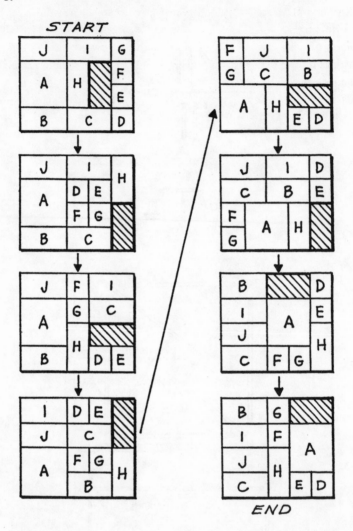

Some intermediate steps are omitted. They can be worked out without difficulty.

6. "Squaring the circle is proclaimed impossible, but what does 'impossible' mean in mathematics? The first steam vessel to cross the Atlantic carried, as part of its cargo, a book that 'proved' it was impossible for a steam vessel to cross anything, much less the Atlantic."—Kasner and Newman in *Mathematics and the Imagination*.

7. Although it may look impossible, it is in fact very simple to get the hook off the string. Take the loop where it passes behind the two strings on which the cup hangs and pull it until you have a loop large enough to pass around the cup. Pull the loop around the cup, from the back forward, and the cup will be released from the string.

8. Not at all. It can be done as follows:

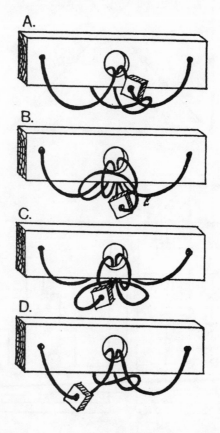

A.

B.

C.

D.

Explanation: Move the block through the loop (position A). Then pull the loop through the hole from the back to the front (position B).

81

Pass the block from right to left through the loops as shown (position C). Pass the loop back through the hole from front to back and the block will now be on the left (position D).

10.

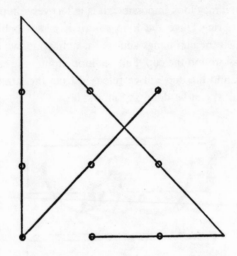

12.

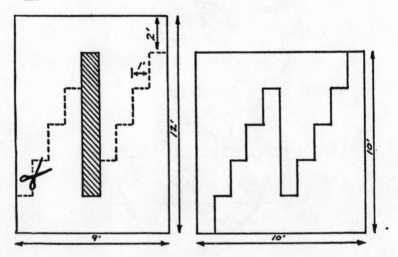

13. To visualize the problem, imagine that the room can be unfolded, like a shoebox, in various ways and that the routes of the spider to the fly can thus be seen as if they were flat. The apparently straightest route (A) is actually the longest—42 feet. Route B requires that the spider travel slightly over 40 feet. Route C, the shortest, is exactly 40 feet.

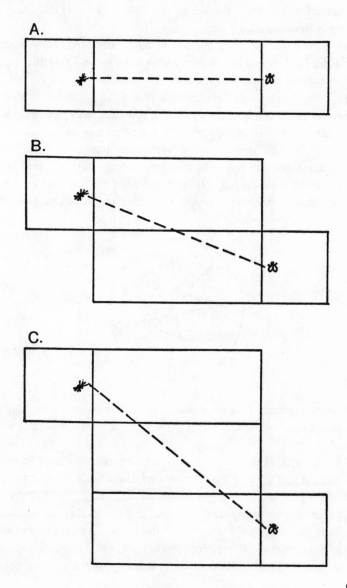

A.

B.

C.

14. Twenty-eight days. On the twenty-eighth day the snail reaches the top of the well. Once there, it does not, of course, slip backward.

15. Three hours and three minutes. Once the amoeba in the first jar has reproduced itself (a process that takes three minutes), that jar is at the same point at which the second jar started. The only difference is that it is three minutes behind.

16. Shame on you if you missed this oldie. Since the ship is afloat, the water level in relation to the ship stays the same. Therefore, eight feet are above the water at the end, just as at the beginning.

17. Pour the five-ounce container full from the jug. Pour the three-ounce container full from the five-ounce container, leaving two ounces remaining in the five-ounce container. Pour the three-ounce container back into the jug. Then pour the two ounces remaining in the five-ounce container into the three-ounce container. Pour the five-ounce container full from the jug. Fill the remaining one ounce of the three-ounce container from the five-ounce container and four ounces are left.

18.

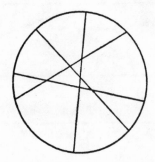

Eleven segments may be formed with the four lines. The key, of course, is that each successive line must divide as many segments as possible.

19. 160 mph. (The secret lies in converting miles per hour to miles per minute and in using fractions instead of decimals to avoid rounding errors.)

20. Assume any convenient distance for the total trip. If, for example, it is thirty miles, the first half of the trip at 15 mph requires one hour. But to average 30 mph for the total trip would require one hour. Therefore the puzzle has no solution; it is impossible.

24.

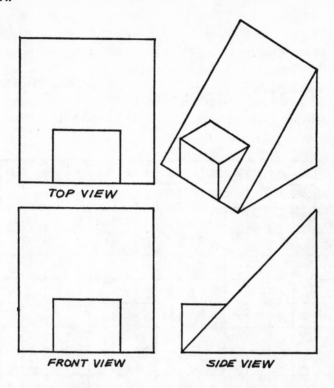

TOP VIEW

FRONT VIEW

SIDE VIEW

25. The shape is simply two intersecting cylinders, one of which has a hole bored through its center:

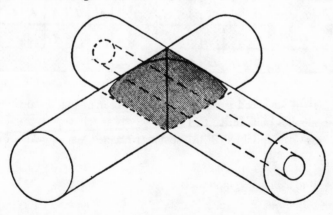

CHAPTER III

1. Strength

2. Facetious

3. Bookkeeper

4. John, while James had had "had," had had "had had." "Had had" had had a better effect on the teacher.

5. All of them contain three consecutive letters of the alphabet.

6.

In cases of advanced frustration the composer of this puzzle sometimes supplies hints for certain of the words as follows:

Across—1. Capital I's (British spelling) 7. One C said quickly = once

8. Greek alphabet 9. Long A = along 16. U = me, to reader 18. Bar G
22. Deuce = 2; 2 C's = seduce 23. Tail on N = entail 25. I on a sphere
   Down—1. Circle R 2. Greek alphabet 3. A on its own = alone 4. E's
joined at the middle = Siamese 5. I on I's 6. D as a bulb = delight 10.
Raise E = erase 12. Brace of pheasants = 2 pheasants; thus embrace.
14. Single R 20. A ditto = ado 22. Sole O.

CHAPTER IV

1. White. It is a polar bear, for the North Pole is one of the places
where you can go one mile south, one mile east, and one mile north,
and still end up at your starting point. (The others are near the South
Pole.)

2. The carpenter must use the full six cuts. To prove this, consider
the middle cube. It must have six faces and each must be made with a
separate cut.

3. Most people erroneously include No. 4 in their answer. But consider: No. 2 does not matter, since the question is concerned only with
red cards. If No. 1 has a circle, the answer to the question is no.
Similarly, if No. 3 is red the answer is no. If No. 1 is a square, No. 3 is
green, and No. 4 is either red *or* green the answer is yes. Therefore the
answer is: No. 1 and No. 3.

4. See Chapter 6 for the solution to this problem.

5. Weigh coins 1, 2, 3, and 4 against coins 5, 6, 7, and 8. If they
balance, weight coins 9 and 10 against coins 11 and 8 (we know from
the first weighing that 8 is a good coin). If they balance, we know coin
12, the only unweighed one, is the counterfeit. The third weighing
indicates whether it is heavy or light.

If, however, at the second weighing (above), coins 11 and 8 are
heavier than coins 9 and 10, either 11 is heavy or 9 is light or 10 is light.
Weigh 9 with 10. If they balance, 11 is heavy. If they don't balance,
either 9 or 10 is light.

Now assume that at first weighing the side with coins 5, 6, 7, and 8 is
heavier than the side with coins 1, 2, 3, and 4. This means that either 1,
2, 3, or 4 is light or 5, 6, 7, or 8 is heavy. Weigh 1, 2, and 5 against 3, 6,
and 9. If they balance, it means that either 7 or 8 is heavy or 4 is light.

By weighing 7 and 8 we obtain the answer, because if they balance then 4 has to be light. If 7 and 8 do not balance, then the heavier coin is the counterfeit.

If, when we weigh 1, 2, and 5 against 3, 6, and 9, the right side is heavier, then either 6 is heavy or 1 is light or 2 is light. By weighing 1 against 2 the solution is obtained.

If, however, when we weigh 1, 2, and 5 against 3, 6, and 9, the right side is lighter, then either 3 is light or 5 is heavy. By weighing 3 against a good coin the solution is easily arrived at.

6. The messenger is a truth teller. If the native in the distance lived on the western side of the island, and was therefore a truth teller, he would say so. If, on the other hand, the native in the distance lived on the eastern side of the island and was therefore a liar, he would say the same thing.

7. The first man, whether or not he is an islander, did say he is white. (Either he *is* white and therefore tells the truth, or he is an islander and lies; the result is the same in either case.) The second man accurately reports what the first man said, so we know the rest of his statement is also true. Therefore he is white and the first man is white. The third man is therefore a liar and a native.

8.

¹3	8	²7	³2	0		⁴5
4		⁵9	1		⁶4	4
0		2		⁷3	8	4
	⁸1	1	⁹1	0		
¹⁰7	2		¹¹1	9	¹²1	¹³8
9				¹⁴7	9	2
¹⁵2	7		¹⁶1	6		9

Explanation ("Across" and "Down" are indicated by "A" and "D"):

Consider 15A. Father Dunk must walk at either 3 or 4 mph, since only these numbers yield a two-digit cube. Assume 4 mph and write 64 for 15A.

Note 11A. The first digit must be 1, since it is a four-digit year and we have not yet reached the year 2000. Then the last digit of 16A is 3, which is also the last digit of 7D. But 7D is a square, and no square ends in 3. Therefore Father Dunk walks at 3 mph, and 15A is 27. (This yields a 6 as the last digit of 7D, possible for a square.)

Notice that 9D times 10A equals 10D. The value for 9D ends in 1 and 10D ends in 2, so that (. . 1) (?)—(. . 2). The only possible second digit for 10A is 2. By reasoning similar to that used for 11A above, we conclude that the first digit of 8A is 1. So 8D is 12. If $1\frac{1}{3}$ the perimeter of Dog's Mead is walked in 12 minutes, then one can go around exactly once in 9 minutes; at 3 mph, that is a distance of 792 yards for the perimeter, 14A.

Consider 11A. The second digit must be an 8 or a 9; otherwise Mary would have been born before 1800, making her over 100 years old, impossible because her age in 1939, 3D, is a two-digit number. Assume the year of her birth is in the 1800s. Then it must have been at least 1839, making the third digit of 11A and the first digit of 12D at least 3. This implies that the three digits of 10D plus 1 are equal to a minimum of 39, impossible for a three-digit number. Therefore, the year of Mary's birth must be 1900 or later, making the second digit of 11A a 9, and making 7D a cube ending in 976.

Since the perimeter is 792 yards, the length plus the breadth equals 396 yards. The breadth must end in a 4 or 6 for its square (7D) to end in 6. Finally, the fact that 6D is two digits indicates that the difference between the length and breadth is less than 100 yards. Only the following dimensions satisfy these three conditions:

Length

242 240 232 230 222 220 212 210 202 200

Breadth

154 156 164 166 174 176 184 186 194 196

Only 176 yields a square ending in 976. So 7D equals 30976, and the dimensions of Dog's Mead are 220 yards by 176 yards. The value for 6A, then, is 44.

From the dimensions of Dog's Mead, it is easily calculated that the area is 32 roods, which, times 12 for 8D, yields 384 for 7A. If Ted's age (6D) is 48, Mary must be 21 for him to be twice her age in 1945. Then 3D is 21, and the year of her birth, 11A, is 1918.

Since the year the Dunks acquired Dog's Mead ends in 0 (8A), the number of years it has been in the family (13D) must end in 9, since the year is 1939. Then, 13D is 829, and 8A becomes 1110. Now 16A can be derived; it equals 16.

Recall that 9D times 10A equals 10D. And, we now see that the three digits of that product plus 1 must equal 19 (12D). Try various digits beginning with 1 for the first digit of 10A. For 1, 10A equals 12, which times 11 (9D) equals 132, whose digits plus 1 add up to 7, which is not equal to 19 (12D). By trial and error, it is found that 10A equals 72, and 10D becomes 792.

The area of Dog's Mead (1A) is 38,720 sq. yds. Note that 1D times the area of 32 roods divided by 20 shillings per pound equals the total value in pounds of Dog's Mead. Since 1D is at least 300 shillings, the value of Dog's Mead is equal to at least 480 pounds, so 4D must begin with a digit at least equal to 5 (otherwise 4D would equal 444 pounds, less than 480 pounds). Try various digits for 4D from 5 upward that will divide evenly by 32 to yield an even value (with no remainder) for 1D. Only 544 pounds works out for 4D, to give 340 for 1D.

All that remains is 2D. The only number having a four-digit square equal to 7—1 is 89, which squares to 7921. So Father Dunk's mother-in-law is 89, his Aunt Martha (5A) is 91, and the problem is done.

9. Black. See Chapter VI.

10. I. J. Good, who supplied this puzzle, explains the solution as follows: "Each person realizes that if the mark on his own forehead were white, then the puzzle for the remaining three people would be precisely the three-person puzzle. Since he knows that they are exceptionally intelligent, he knows they would be able to solve this puzzle. After a few minutes, since none of them has in fact solved it, he realizes that the mark on his own forehead must be black." Mr. Good (who is, incidentally, a University Professor in the Department of Statistics at Virginia Polytechnic Institute) adds: "The puzzle cannot be extended to five people. Even if all five are told that they are all exceptionally intelligent, there is no guarantee at any time that the others would have been able to solve the four-person puzzle."

11. Gloria loves Arthur.

12. There are 10 birds and 20 animals. The problem may be expressed in equation form as follows, letting A represent animals and B represent birds:

$$A + B = 30$$
$$4A + 2B = 100$$

13. Harry is the pitcher, Allen the catcher, Paul the first baseman, Jerry the second baseman, Andy the third baseman, Ed the shortstop, Sam the left fielder, Mike the right fielder, and Bill the center fielder.

14. The fly traveled two miles. See Chapter VI.

15. It can't be done. See Chapter VI.

16. He asks either man, "If I were to ask you if this is the way I should go, would you say yes?" If the man he asks is the one who tells the truth, he will of course get the right answer. If the man he asks is the man who always lies, that man lies about the answer he would give, thus giving the correct answer. By forcing the liar to lie twice, one lie negating the other, the man forces him to tell the truth.

17. Three.

CHAPTER V

1. See Chapter VI.

2. 9567
   + 1085
   ‾‾‾‾‾
   10652

3. The extra square results from the slight inaccuracy of the drawing of just one line, or from the mental assumption that the hypotenuses of the two smaller triangles are in an exact straight line. The discrepancy amounts to about 3 per cent of the large triangle's area.

4. All of the numbers are the number 16, written in different bases. The first is written in the base 16, the second in the base 15, etc., down to the last, which is written in the base 1. The missing number, therefore, is 121.

5. (c)

6. 50 minutes.

7. 1 lb., 3 lbs., 9 lbs., and 27 lbs. In most cases, of course, various combinations of weights must be put on both sides of the scale.

8. 17 men, 13 women, 90 children.

9. 5³/₄ inches long.

10. 40 mph.

11. About 5³/₄ inches.

12. (a) The rudimentary formula that brought an end to inexact tallying of possessions or exchange.

(b) Sir Isaac Newton's formula for gravitation.

(c) Einstein's formula for the conversion of matter to energy.

(d) John Napier's logarithm formula, which provided a multiplication and division method simply by adding or subtracting the logarithms of numbers.

(e) Pythagoras' formula for the relationship of the two sides and hypotenuse of a right triangle.

(f) Ludwig Boltzmann's equation for the behavior of gases.

(g) Konstantin Tsiolkovskii's equation giving the changing speed of a rocket as it burns the weight of its fuel.

(h) Louis de Broglie's equation for light as a form of energy.

(i) James Clerk Maxwell's formula equating electricity and magnetism.

(j) Archimedes' formula for the lever.

13. See Chapter VI.

CHAPTER VII

1. d

2. c

3. e

4. b

5. d

6. d
7. b
8. b
9. a
10. e
11. d
12. c
13. a
14. c
15. c
16. b
17. c
18. a

More Games
for the
Superintelligent

For Alice,
who is superintelligent
in the only way that really counts

A word of welcome—
and of warning

There are, I have discovered, two kinds of people in the
world: those who love puzzles and those who can't stand
them.* This would hardly be worth bringing up if it were not
for the fact that the two camps are so distinct, and indeed
even hostile, as to present more than ordinary dangers for the
unwary. Puzzles lovers, despite the convolutions and complexities of their minds, tend in one respect to be quite simple
people. We naïvely assume that because *we* like puzzles, and
because puzzles seem to us so self-evidently pleasurable,
surely everybody must like them. In fact, however, everybody
does no such thing. On the contrary, many people, upon
being shown a puzzle, even one of unquestionable excellence,
will turn upon it—and upon us—with such scorn that we are
likely to think long and hard before proffering another one. I
myself have seen the eyes of more than one friend glaze over
with boredom when confronted with my enthusiasm for puzzles. I even know of a marriage whose untimely dissolution

* There are also, of course, two *other* kinds of people in the world: those
who believe there are two kinds of people in the world and those who do
not. That, however, is an entirely different subject.

was at least partly attributable to one of the partners' over-fondness for mental recreations, and another in which one member, finally grown impatient at her spouse's insistence that she share his intellectual romps, was driven to declare, "If you ever show me another one of those puzzles I swear I'm going to move as far away from you as I can. Maybe to Pago Pago." (He did and she did, though not to Pago Pago. The anecdote seems to me, however, to lose little of its force because of that minor imperfection.)

Such misadventures are clearly indicative of strong feelings —ones we toy with at our peril. Be forewarned, therefore: the mere fact that you are reading this book by no means grants you license to urge its contents on those who are not similarly committed. The only safe procedure is to acknowledge the fact that in your liking for puzzles you are different from other people. Revel privately, if you want to, in that difference, but do not—under any circumstances—undertake even the gentlest of proselytizing. That way lies nothing but disaster. Remember: you are an intellectual at play, not a missionary.

The sort of hostility I am speaking of is nothing new. As long ago as the tenth century, an Arab traveler named Ibn Fadlan, visiting the Volga Bulgars, reported: "When they observe a man who excels through quickwittedness and knowledge, they . . . seize him, put a rope around his neck and hang him on a tree where he is left until he rots away." Lest anyone wonder why the Bulgars recoiled so strongly from any display of excessive intelligence, Zeki Validi Togan, an authority on Ibn Fadlan, explains: "There is nothing mysterious about the cruel treatment meted out by the Bulgars to people who were overly clever. It was based on the simple, sober reasoning of the average citizens who wanted only to lead what they considered to be a normal life, and to avoid any risk or adventure in which the 'genius' might lead them."

As the intelligentsia of Ibn Fadlan's time learned to their distress, the temptation to share one's enthusiasms is always great—sometimes too great. When a thing gives us as much pleasure as puzzles and other mental diversions can, it is only natural that we should want to spread the word. Resist that temptation. I speak from experience. Some time ago, on a beach near Sarasota, Florida, I was using a conch shell to sketch a puzzle in the sand for a friend. It was a complicated puzzle, and I had covered considerable wind-swept acreage with diagrams, charts, and computations when I paused to look up—just in time to see my friend pile the last of his beach gear into his car and drive off.

That sort of thing has an ugly way of sticking in your mind. What lesson, if any, can we draw from it? Well, for one thing it suggests, I think, that we must choose our puzzle companions with care. We must not assume, until we have seen irrefutable evidence of it, the presence of an enthusiasm that may not exist at all. Rather, those of us who share an interest in puzzles should stick quietly together, welcoming outsiders whenever they chance to turn up, but never taking it for granted that they will. (They usually won't.) I have discovered, just as you no doubt have, that fooling around with puzzles is an essentially solitary pastime. In the predecessor to this book, *Games for the Superintelligent,* I briefly mentioned the solitariness of the puzzler's lot and was instantly awash in correspondents grateful at having found some kindred spirits at last. The loneliness of the puzzler is, it seems, an inseparable part of his condition.

This view was convincingly buttressed just as I was getting ready to write these words. In a letter from Oak Park, Illinois, a reader wrote as follows:

> I greatly enjoyed your book. Although I never have considered myself a genius, your discussion of the problems encountered by very bright people had a familiar ring. I tried every problem in your book and solved a large number of them. This was a great boost to my spirit. I have never been much of a conversationalist, nor a mixer. Frankly, most people bore me after a short time, and I had always wondered why this was and what was wrong with me and why I was different. I will be forever grateful to you for helping me find some answers to my questions.

Not everyone, of course, is going to find answers to his fundamental puzzlements about life in a book like this one. What most people *will* find is something quite different, though in its way it is also valuable: a kind of puzzle not readily available elsewhere. The title of this volume is, needless to say, something of a jape, intended (1) to flatter the reader and (2) to suggest that he will in turn be flattering anyone for whom he buys it as a gift. Yet, that ugly little secret having been confessed, there remains one sense in which the title is quite accurate: these are a peculiar sort of puzzle. They all have a proven appeal for extremely bright people, either the members of Mensa, the high-I.Q. society whose puzzles inspired *Games for the Superintelligent,* or else the young professional men and women who subscribe to the four magazines for which I have edited a monthly puzzle column for some three years now.* The puzzles are all, furthermore, rigorously logical and, except for those in Chapter VI, free from trickery and attempts to mislead. They are, furthermore, essentially simple, requiring no advanced mathematics and no knowledge of esoteric logical principles. Finally, they all have a clean, spare elegance: they are not rock but plainsong.

If your tastes are at all like mine, you'll enjoy these puzzles. Most puzzle books, even those intended for more or less intelligent readers, are woefully unappealing. The other day, while doing a bit of rearranging in my library, I found myself trying to gather all my puzzle books together in one place. They made a considerable pile, but not, I am sorry to say, a very interesting one. Most of the books seemed to have been put together by worshipers of mere doggedness, the sort of people who find it fun to hunt for hidden words in bleak and meaningless prairies of jumbled letters. The words can be found, of course, but to what purpose? When you are through, all you have proved is that you can keep your mind on a dull subject for a long time.

But *de gustibus,* etc. If people enjoy that sort of thing, let us rejoice on their behalf. Pleasure, any pleasure, is all too rare in this world. Yet we need not seek to share that particular pleasure. I have, on the contrary, taken pains to avoid that kind of puzzle, on the grounds that an intricate and precise logical excursion, however brief, is more rewarding than a whole afternoon spent slogging purposelessly through some protracted problem fit only for drones. I make no apology for

* *Juris Doctor* (for lawyers), *MBA* (business executives), *Medical Dimensions* (doctors), and *New Engineer* (engineers of all types). Together they reach several hundred thousand readers, most of them, to judge by the mail I receive, both enthusiastic about puzzles and impressively knowledgeable about them.

taking this severe and limited view of things. There are plenty of books for the drones and far too few for you and me.

A word about how this volume is arranged. It seems to me that, since human intelligence is our subject, we ought first to try to reach some agreement on exactly what it is. Accordingly, the first chapter takes us into that fascinating and perennially controversial mine field. There follow several sizable clumps of puzzles of various types—mathematical, verbal, logical, and so forth—all of them arranged to give the reader's mind a varied and vigorous regimen of calisthenics. Since some readers, by the time they are this far into things, may well be wondering why they are having trouble with certain puzzles and not with others, they will next find a chapter dealing with the techniques of puzzle solving; it gives, among other things, a good many examples of the ways extremely bright people attack a puzzle and how their minds differ from those of the less nimble-witted among us. Finally, in Chapter VIII, you will find an intelligence test that will give an indication of your fitness for membership in perhaps the most exclusive intellectual club the world has ever known: Mensa. To join, you don't need wealth, looks, or even good manners. All you need is an I.Q. in the top 2 per cent of the population. If you measure up, you may find the organization just the thing for learning what your mind is made of. If, either because of heredity or inclination, the verbal hurly-burly of Mensa isn't your kind of competition, do at least stay for the preliminary rounds in Chapters I to VI. You could, in spite of yourself, discover that what you had always thought was just gray matter is really something considerably more colorful.

JAMES F. FIXX

Riverside, Connecticut

Contents

I

What, exactly, is intelligence?

Even though you and I have a fairly clear idea of what we mean when we use the word "intelligence," there has never been much scholarly agreement on just what intelligence really is. Sir Francis Galton, a pioneer investigator of the human brain and the author of *Hereditary Genius: An Enquiry into its Laws and Consequences* (1869), thought of intelligence as being made up of three separate qualities—"intellect," "zeal," and "power of work." C. E. Spearman, the inventor of factor analysis and author of *The Abilities of Man* (1927), considered intelligence to be something—he called it simply *g*—accounting for the fact that a person who does well at one thing is also likely to do well at other things. L. L. Thurstone, the author of *The Nature of Intelligence* (1924), believed intelligence to be composed of precisely seven capacities, verbal ability, verbal fluency, numerical ability, spatial ability, perceptual ability, inductive reasoning, and memory. On the other hand, J. P. Guilford, a psychologist who has had considerable influence during the past quarter century, purported to find in intelligence no fewer than 120 abilities, which he cross-classified into (a) the types of information each customarily handles, (b) the process by which it handles it, and (c) the nature of what emerges. Other researchers, a bit less ambitiously, have tried to get off to a solid start by offering workable definitions of intelligence, but with equally disparate results. It has, for example, been called "the ability to carry on abstract thinking" by L. M. Terman, "the capacity to acquire capacity" by Herbert Woodrow, and "innate general cognitive ability" by C. L. Burt. Spearman called it "the ability to educe relations and correlates," and James McKeen Cattell tried to clarify matters by distinguishing between "fluid" and "crystallized" intelligence.

Intelligence is unquestionably a curiously elusive human capacity. Any one of us can easily recognize intelligence when we encounter it, and can unhesitatingly judge, furthermore, whether it is in deficient supply or is present in abundance. Yet those who have devoted their lives to its study cannot tell us whether it is one thing or 120 separate things and cannot, for that matter, even agree on a definition. It is, however, too easy, as well as distinctly misleading, to make a joke of what is a serious, fundamentally valid, and certainly arduous enterprise. Coming to grips with intelligence is no easy task. The chief problem is that it is not directly observable. We cannot place calipers on it to measure it, nor can an anatomist evaluate it at an autopsy. It is detectable, if it is detectable at all, only in the results it produces. The Encyclopaedia Britannica calls it a "hypothetical construct" and points out that even I.Q., which many imagine to be a quite unambiguous assessment of a person's intelligence, is nothing more than a "representation" of intelligence. A representation, it goes without saying, may be quite unlike the real thing.

Part of the difficulty arises from the fact that intelligence—and its more awesome partner, genius—got off to a bad start, or at any rate a late one. Although the early Babylonian writers and the Greek philosophers discussed the intellect, the mind, and related questions, the present-day concept of intelligence was unknown until the early years of the twentieth century. The word "genius," in the sense in which we most commonly use it today, did not even appear in Samuel Johnson's exhaustive dictionary of 1755. (The 1971 OED, which does of course include it, defines it as "native intellectual power of an exalted type, such as is attributed to those who are esteemed greatest in any department of art, speculation, or practice; instinctive and extraordinary capacity for imaginative creation, original thought, invention, or discovery," and goes on to observe that it is "often contrasted with *talent*.") Intelligence, it seems, was a subject that simply did not arise until the twentieth century's analytical spirit finally called it into being.

When that happened, it was only natural that researchers should be as interested in measuring its dimensions as in describing how it works. Our age, after all, is one in which it is seen as a proper function of scholarship not just to explain Shakespeare but, using computers, to dissect him syllable by syllable—and there are no doubt some who, if a choice had to be made, would argue that the latter should take precedence. So the Intelligence Quotient—that number that haunts our lives from kindergarten to crypt—was born. In concept anyway, the I.Q. seems quite straightforward. To start with, one assumes that intelligence is distributed along a Gaussian curve, with perhaps slightly more people at the low-I.Q. end to account for brain damage (which diminishes I.Q. but does not, so far as we know, ever raise it). If we let 100 represent average intelligence, then 50 per cent of the world's population is seen to have I.Q.s between 90 and 110, 68 per cent between 85 and 115, 14 per cent between 116 and 130, and 2 per cent above 130. If, then, we devise reliable I.Q. tests, each of us can readily be placed in his proper place on the bell-shaped curve and can enjoy the benefits—or endure the consequences—appropriate to that station. It all seems to make a good deal of sense.

Unfortunately, the first I.Q. test had scarcely been devised (by the French psychologist Alfred Binet, in 1905) than a backlash began to set in. By midcentury it was at full strength. In 1958 David Wechsler, chief psychologist at Bellevue Psychiatric Hospital, was writing (in *The Measurement and Appraisal of Adult Intelligence*), "In recent years the I.Q. has lost caste. There has been a growing tendency among clinical psychologists to pay only scant attention to the I.Q. as such." More recently, I.Q. tests have come in for heavy criticism on political grounds. In his recent book *The Science and Politics of I.Q.*, Leon J. Kamin defines the issue succinctly: "The I.Q. test in America, and the way in which we think about it, has been fostered by men committed to a particular social view. That view includes the belief that those on the bottom are genetically inferior victims of their own immutable defects. The consequence has been that the I.Q. test has served as an instrument of oppression against the poor—dressed in the trappings of science, rather than politics. The message of science is heard respectfully, particularly when the tidings it carries are soothing to the public conscience." Far from being, as one American psychologist has called it, "psychology's most telling accomplishment," the I.Q. test is, in this view, wickedly fraudulent.

One need not be a psychologist to discern another way in which I.Q. tests can be misleading. Most people, especially laymen, customarily refer to a person's I.Q. as if it were always a valid indication of ability. But a moment's reflection will reveal that it is no such thing. We all know people of unquestioned brilliance who can hardly cross the street without endangering their lives (it is for good reason that the absent-minded professor is a persistent folk figure) and other people who, although commanding a vast body of information and uncommon mental agility, are scarcely able to earn a living. There is, in short, not necessarily much of a correlation between I.Q. and ability. The most sophisticated psychologists are, of course, well aware of this and put little emphasis on I.Q. in the absence of other information about a person. Writes Wechsler: "Individuals having the same I.Q.'s may differ considerably in their actual or potential capacity for intelligent behavior." He leaves no doubt about exactly what he means: "Every reader will be able to recall persons of high intellectual ability in some particular field whom they would unhesitatingly characterize as below average in general intelligence."

If, then, the experts are not agreed on just what intelligence is, and if, furthermore, the dowsing rod that is supposed to find it doesn't work after all, can we even presume to discuss it? Can it be of any possible interest to us? Can we make any use of the concept, fuzzy as it plainly is? The answer to all three questions is: Of course we can. Psychologists may tie themselves into knots trying to define intelligence, and they may worry about what precisely belongs in the recipe, whether a single ingredient or 120 of them, but as a practical matter you and I know we have no such difficulty. We freely discuss intelligence with each other, knowing at least in a general way what we are talking about. (If our talk lacks scientific precision, that is only because we ordinarily have no need for such precision. I do not need to know the words *Cyanocitta cristata* in order to tell you there is a blue jay in my bird feeder.) Furthermore, we have little difficulty in agreeing on what constitutes intelligence and what does not. We are amazed, perhaps, by the story of Jacques Inaudi, whom Binet studied at length in 1892 and 1893 because in fifteen minutes the young man could do mathematical calculations that would have taken a first-rate mathematician fifteen days. But we never mistake such isolated abilities for the sort of broad intelligence possessed by Leonardo da Vinci or Newton or, in our own time, Einstein.

We can agree, too, on at least one other thing: intelligence is well worth having. Intelligence has, to be sure, landed more than a few of its possessors in deep trouble. One thinks, for example, of the student who on a physics examination was asked to describe a method for determining the height of a building by using a barometer. Finding the expected answer obvious and uninteresting, he outraged the educational authorities by giving two alternate methods: (1) drop the barometer off the building's roof and time the interval until it smashes on the ground; (2) find the owner of the building and say to him, "If you tell me how tall your building is, I will give you a good barometer."* One thinks, too, of the seventeenth-century Dominican friar Giordano Bruno, who was offered one opportunity after another to renounce the heresies of Copernicanism and thereby save his life. Ultimately Bruno,

* Eddie Epstein of New York City proposes a third method: find the owner of the building and say to him, "If you don't tell me how tall your building is, I'll break this barometer over your head."

unwilling to violate what his vast, inquiring intellect told him must be true, was burned at the stake by the Inquisition.

For the most part, however, such painful exceptions notwithstanding, intelligence is beyond question something to be prized. Studies show that those who are gifted as children earn above-average incomes as adults, enjoy better mental and physical health, and do better both in school and at work. Not long ago a Stanford University professor, Dr. Pauline S. Sears, reported on the results of a continuing study of 430 women who, as teen-agers in California in the 1920s, were in the top 1 per cent of the population in intelligence. (The study, regarded as a classic, was begun in 1921–22 by Stanford psychologist L. M. Terman.) Dr. Sears found that 67 per cent of them had earned bachelors' degrees (8 per cent is typical for their age group) and that they had, by their own testimony, lived more satisfying lives than would have been the case had they been less intellectually gifted. "It may well be," she wrote in a report on the study, "that the coping mechanisms which enable gifted women to adapt flexibly to a variety of conditions . . . are related to the intelligence they bring to their life situations."

One need not, however, take so pragmatic a view of intelligence in order to find it worth while. In his lively and wide-ranging study, *Anti-Intellectualism in American Life,* Richard Hofstadter refers to the capacity for intellectual "playfulness": "The intellectual relishes the play of the mind for its own sake, and finds in it one of the major values in life. What one thinks of here is the element of sheer delight in intellectual activity. Seen in this guise, intellect may be taken as the healthy animal spirits of the mind, which come into exercise when the surplus of mental energies is released from the tasks required for utility and mere survival. . . . Veblen spoke often of the intellectual faculty as 'idle curiosity'—but this is a misnomer in so far as the curiosity of the playful mind is inordinately restless and active. This very restlessness and activity gives a distinctive cast to its view of truth and its discontent with dogmas." Intelligence, it is plain, finds abundant justification not in (to use Hofstadter's archly playful word) "mere" usefulness but in pure frolicsomeness and *joie de vivre*.

We thus find ourselves in the curious position of children who, seeing a person eat an unknown food, want some for themselves and start screaming for it: we may not know what intelligence is but we want more of it—for ourselves, certainly, but especially for our offspring. But how much more can we have? Is it possible to enhance or increase what we have been given? It is easy to agree with Leonardo's observation: "Iron rusts from disuse, stagnant water loses its purity and in cold weather becomes frozen; even so does inaction sap the vigors of the mind." But is the corollary equally true? Can exercise, perhaps certain mental disciplines, stimulate the vigors of the mind?

Many people would say yes. "There is a technique, a knack, for thinking. . . ," Charles P. Curtis, Jr., and Ferris Greenslet wrote in their charming anthology *The Practical Cogitator*. "You are not wholly at the mercy of your thoughts. . . . They are a machine you can learn to operate." Similarly, Win Wenger, in his recent book *How to Increase Your Intelligence,* has little doubt that we can improve our I.Q.s. Noting that intelligence is the result of heredity (80 per cent or so) and environment (the remaining 20 per cent or so), and that these seem to be more or less rigidly fixed at an

112

early age, Wenger is nonetheless certain we can do something about our intelligence: "There is a misconception that we are born with a certain intelligence and are trapped forever in the narrow range that is determined to be our 'I.Q.' The truth of the matter is that unless we are taught to use our brains, unless we fully understand how our brains work and their relationship to intelligence, we may never even approach truly intelligent functioning. Within all of us is the potential for genius."*

This seems to me rather doubtful. Geniuses, by definition, are so extraordinary that it takes very little acquaintance with even a single genius to realize that most of us are light-years from their mental estate. I once had the opportunity of working closely with a person who was unquestionably a genius. He had a nimble, inventive, and above all tireless mind, and one of my strongest memories is of watching our little staff, myself included, crumble into collapsed quiescence as the night wore on, while he remained as fresh as he had been when he showed up for work that morning. "He seems," a staff member remarked after one particularly long night, "to have some secret source of energy that no one else has learned how to draw on." As a chronic and lifelong eight-hour sleeper, I cannot imagine anything (even brachiation) that could possibly boost me to the kind of sleepless genius my colleague enjoyed.

---

* Wenger's is a heady and uplifting doctrine. But not every reader, I suspect, will be inclined to follow every aspect of the intellectual regimen he prescribes—particularly when it comes to such I.Q.-raising techniques as hanging upside down with your eyes closed (to improve circulation in the brain and build up its "balancing centers") and brachiation, or swinging from one overhead handhold to another like an ape (to "turn on" the cortex).

On the other hand, there seems little doubt that one can improve the functioning of the brain at least to some extent. In my own case, I have been studying puzzles and I.Q. tests for so long that even the toughest and trickiest of them are likely to be more or less familiar to me. By one definition, then (I.Q. is what an I.Q. test tests), my I.Q. has indeed improved. I grant you that the improvement is largely spurious—being able to solve a tricky puzzle does not, after all, equip a person to live more rationally—but in this one respect my brain is a more efficient instrument. That sort of improvement is within the reach of anyone who wants to take the trouble.

Whether it is worth taking the trouble for is the question. Many experts would argue that it is not. David Wechsler summarily disposes of such ambitions by his reference to *"artificially* raising the I.Q. test *score"* (the emphasis is his), clearly implying a distinction between actual I.Q. and one's I.Q. score. To raise the score without affecting the I.Q. is much like congratulating yourself on having grown taller merely because you've bought yourself a pair of elevator shoes.

Other mental techniques, however, confer more solid benefits. The German physicist Helmholtz, whose researches ranged widely over the whole landscape of science, once told how important new thoughts came to him. He described three steps. The first he called Preparation, in which he investigated the problem "in all directions." The second was Incubation, in which he did no conscious thinking about the problem. The third he called Illumination; it was then that "happy ideas come unexpectedly without effort, like an inspiration." Helmholtz went on to remark, "So far as I am concerned, they have never come to me when my mind was fatigued, or when

I was at my working table." Ideas came most easily to him, he said, during a walk in the woods on a sunny day. Arthur Koestler described much the same process in *The Act of Creation*; its general outlines will be familiar to anyone who, working with his brain, must rely not just on doggedness but on an occasional flicker of inspiration.

Graham Wallas, an English economist who was much concerned with the role of the subconscious, thought the process Helmholtz describes could be consciously controlled. "Men have known for thousands of years," he wrote, "that conscious effort and its resulting habits can be used to improve the thought-processes of young persons, and have formulated for that purpose an elaborate art of education. The 'educated' man can, in consequence, 'put his mind on' to a chosen subject, and 'turn his mind off' in a way which is impossible to an uneducated man." Wallas suggested that the problem-solving process can be made more efficient by starting to work on several problems in succession, then laying them aside, rather than trying to solve a problem at one sitting.* The important thing is that there be a period of freedom from the demands of the problem at hand, a time of leisure and even of idleness. How much may Darwin's lifelong poor health, and his conse-

* Wallas offers two enlightening illustrations, one showing what the Helmholtz technique can accomplish, the other showing what happens when it is ignored: "A well-known academic psychologist . . . , who was also a preacher, told me that he found by experience that his Sunday sermon was much better if he posed the problem on Monday, than if he did so later in the week, although he might give the same number of hours of conscious work to it in each case. It seems to be a tradition among practicing barristers to put off any consideration of each brief to the latest possible moment before they have to deal with it, and to forget the whole matter as rapidly as possible after dealing with it. This fact may help to explain a certain want of depth which has often been noticed in the typical lawyer-statesman, and which may be due to his conscious thought not being sufficiently extended and enriched by subconscious thought."

quent need for frequent rest, have contributed to his achievements?

Although the need for occasional leisured stretches is well known to creative people, it is a constant source of perplexity, and at times impatience, to those who must pay their salaries. I once worked for a publishing company whose president—a businessman at heart, rather than a man of letters—had collected a whole filing drawer full of techniques for prodding indolent writers and editors into giving him a fair day's work. Over the years he had clipped them out of *Advertising Age,* management magazines, and the plethora of newsletters he subscribed to, and he felt that his way with "the creatives," as he called them, was largely attributable to the techniques he had derived from these sources. He had, for one thing, read somewhere that creatives like money as much as anyone else, and he had hopes of someday devising a financial incentive plan for them, much like the commission or bonus arrangement used with salesmen. Once, in an effort to stir a sluggish artist into action, he worked out a custom-tailored plan of Talmudic complexity. When the artist, unmoved, went on as usual, the president confided to me, "Creatives aren't like other people."

He was, of course, right. While writers, editors, painters, composers, and other thinkers may indeed like money as much as anyone else, they are not appreciably moved or motivated by it because in the nature of things they cannot be. When I am seated at my typewriter and the words refuse to come—when, let us say, I am tired or preoccupied or out of sorts—I would welcome a raise in pay but it would almost certainly not improve my work. What does sometimes improve my work is resort to the Helmholtz principle. If I lay the difficulty aside for a time, when I return to it I will in all likelihood find myself able to tackle it with surprising ease. Although this principle is widely applicable, it is one that not many people ever discover—an unfortunate lapse, since using it is precisely equivalent to increasing your intelligence.

The enhancement of intelligence is not, however, without its difficulties and even dangers. This is nowhere truer than in the United States. From the very beginning, the egalitarian idea upon which the nation was founded tended to inhibit any manifestation of extraordinary intelligence. If every man was just as good as every other man, so ran the unexpressed argument, every man was also just as ordinary. With the growing sentiment for universal suffrage in the nineteenth century, the common man began to assume a particularly exalted position. "If reason is a universal faculty," wrote George Bancroft, a nineteenth-century historian who was much involved in the politics of his time, "the universal decision is the nearest criterion of truth. The common mind winnows opinions; it is the sieve which separates error from certainty." Important as this idea unquestionably was in the development of democracy, it did little to enhance the life of the mind. "Anti-intellectualism," observes one historian, "is founded in the democratic institutions and the egalitarian sentiments of this country."

This strain in American life, though persistent, is not, however, quite as anti-intellectual as its critics sometimes pretend. If it were, we might have less to worry about than we actually do. Anti-intellectualism, after all, implies a certain intellectual stance, however wrongheaded. What we find in the United States is something more insidious than anti-intellectualism: a persistent lack of interest in things intellectual. Hofstadter

117

puts it well: "The public is not simply divided into intellectual and anti-intellectual factions. The greater part of the public, and a great part even of the intelligent and alert public, is simply non-intellectual." In his classic study *The Organization Man* (1956), William H. Whyte, Jr., suggests how this attitude manifests itself in business. He cites, as one example, a well-known chemical company's recruiting film. At one point, as three scientists are shown in a laboratory, a narrator comments: "No geniuses here—just a bunch of average Americans working together."

In such a climate, it is scarcely surprising that intelligent people often feel that they receive less recognition than is their due. Not long ago I had a chance to speak with a group of extremely bright adults in New York City. All had I.Q.s of about 150; all worked for large companies; and all spoke feelingly of the necessity for disguising from their superiors the true scope of their mental abilities. "I've found that it's safer," a bearded technician in his thirties said, "not to make waves. Unless you've got a very bright boss, which I don't, you'll just make him feel insecure. I used to try to point out better ways of doing things, but I found that it usually works out better if I keep my ideas to myself." Others in the group echoed his lament.

Our educational system does little to help. In general, it does not do much to raise bright people to their potential nor does it significantly help people of average intelligence understand and appreciate those who are more intelligent than themselves. Though much lip service is given to the importance of educating gifted young people, things have not really changed much in the decade and a half since Jerome S. Bruner, the noted Harvard education professor, wrote that "the top quarter of public school students, from which we must draw intellectual leadership in the next generation, is perhaps the most neglected by our schools. . . ."

The problem is as much a matter of attitude as of practice. It was an official of the U. S. Office of Education who, in a report, blandly lumped together "the blind and the partially seeing, the deaf and the hard of hearing, the speech-defective, the crippled, the delicate, the epileptic, the mentally deficient, the socially maladjusted, and the extraordinarily gifted"— strange bedfellows indeed.

All this would perhaps not matter much if intelligence invariably triumphed over all obstacles, but of course it does not. Intelligence does, it is true, stand up for its rights more stubbornly than one might expect, rising above inept teachers, boring classes, and tiresome jobs. Nonetheless, an inhospitable environment can cause it serious and sometimes irreparable harm. Even a hospitable environment, for that matter, does not guarantee that the full range of a person's intelligence will be called into play. Fatigue, illness, boredom, or just plain laziness can have a considerable effect on how much one accomplishes.* So can the vagaries of the mind. James Harvey Robinson, a historian much concerned with the play and interplay of ideas, writes amusingly of the difference between Kant's "pure reason" and what actually takes place when we think: "Let us forget for the moment any impressions we may have derived from the philosophers, and see what seems

---

* Hallowell Bowser tells the story of the Harvard student who, unable to get an assignment ready by the appointed day, explained to the professor, "I had planned to have my paper finished today but I wasn't feeling very well." "Young man," replied the professor, fixing him with an unsympathetic eye, "you will find, when you have had more experience with life, that most of the world's work is done by people who aren't feeling very well."

119

to happen in ourselves. The first thing that we notice is that our thought moves with such incredible rapidity that it is almost impossible to arrest any specimen of it long enough to have a look at it. When we are offered a penny for our thoughts, we always find that we have recently had so many things in mind that we can easily make a selection that will not compromise us too nakedly. On inspection we shall find that even if we are not downright ashamed of a great part of our spontaneous thinking, it is far too intimate, personal, ignoble, or trivial to permit us to reveal more than a small part of it. . . . We find it hard to believe that other people's thoughts are as silly as our own, but they probably are."

So far we have concerned ourselves largely with obstacles to the functioning of human intelligence: the American egalitarian tradition, with its mistrust of excessive braininess; our educational system, with its confusions in the face of unusual intelligence; and the quirky ways in which the mind itself works. Despite these obstacles and others, however, some minds manage to work wonderfully well. I am indebted to Ivan Schuller of Evanston, Illinois, for an anecdote illustrative of the mathematical mind at work. Writes Mr. Schuller:

> The following question was put to the distinguished mathematician von Neumann by one of his students: Two cyclists start cycling, simultaneously, from the two ends of a 100-mile-long road. They bicycle at a speed of forty miles per hour. At the moment they start, a fly leaves one of the bicycles and starts flying back and forth between the two cyclists until they meet. If the fly travels at 60 miles an hour,

how many miles does it fly before the cyclists meet? One should not, of course, try to add up the infinite series. All you have to do is figure that the cyclists meet in an hour and a quarter and that the fly travels 75 miles in that time. When von Neumann heard the problem he instantaneously gave the right answer. His student said, "It is very strange but everybody tries to add up the infinite series." "What do you mean 'strange'?" von Neumann replied. "That's how I did it."

In my correspondence with puzzle enthusiasts I have found that though not all manifestations of genius are as celebrated as von Neumann's, they may be equally amusing. People whose names you and I have never heard of repeatedly demonstrate that they take a full measure of delight in the play of the mind. In one of my puzzle columns I described a zoo containing thirty birds and animals with a total of 100 feet and asked how many birds and how many animals there were. The answer, obtainable by the use of two simple equations, was meant to be twenty animals and ten birds, but for Nasim Ahmed of Stillwater, Oklahoma, that was too obvious (and not enough fun). His answer: thirty animals, no birds. The animals he had in mind were a centipede and twenty-nine boa constrictors.

Another correspondent cites a different question but gives an equally inventive answer. His question:

You are a captain in charge of one sergeant and four men. Your task is to raise a 100-foot flagpole, sliding it into a hole ten feet deep. You have two ropes—one 22 feet long and one 26 feet long—and two shovels and two buckets. How do you accomplish this?

My correspondent's solution: "You say, 'Sergeant, get that flagpole up.'"

Martin Antila of Bridgeport, Connecticut, also delights in the pleasures of the mind, to judge by a communication he sent me not long ago. "There are ten ravens on the roof of a house," Mr. Antila begins with a perfectly straight face. "A hunter shoots one of them with his rifle. How many of the ravens are left on the roof?" Mr. Antila, proving that things are seldom what they seem, provides four alternate answers.

Answer No. 1: None, if the dead one falls off and the rest fly away.

Answer No. 2: Ten, if the roof is so flat that the dead raven doesn't fall off and the shot is fired from so far away that the rest of the ravens aren't scared away by the shot.

Answer No. 3: One, if the roof is so flat that the dead raven doesn't fall off and the shot is so loud that the live ones are frightened away.

Answer No. 4: Nine, if the roof is so steep that the dead one falls off and the shot is so quiet that the nine don't hear it and fly away.

Whatever intelligence is finally judged to be, it is certainly in some way a major component of mental gymnastics like these. It is clear, I am happy to say, that intelligence, in these delightfully playful forms, flourishes despite all the hazards and obstacles we have been discussing.

That salutary phenomenon, as we shall see, is exactly what this book is all about.

II

On logic, subways, and
going forward by going sideways

One of my favorite puzzles, despite the fact that it contains a geographical wrinkle that renders it unfair under most circumstances, asks simply that you supply the next number in the series 4, 14, 23, 34, and 42. After experimenting with various intervals, fiddling with countless possible relationships, and finally discovering that the numbers apparently constitute no ordinary series, most intelligent people will find themselves turning at last to more remote possibilities. What, exactly, *are* those numbers? People's ages? House numbers? Years with some special significance? It is only at this point that the solver—provided he is familiar with the New York City subway system—is prepared to see that they are the street numbers of the stops on the Sixth Avenue and Eighth Avenue lines (and that the next stop is 50th Street).

Though that puzzle is, of course, uncommonly obscure, it illustrates an important aspect of the best of the variety of puzzle that depends primarily on logic for a solution: at first glance many of them appear to be impossible to solve. Either you don't seem to have enough information, or else they look so difficult that you imagine they would require the entire M.I.T. faculty to come up with an answer, or else some other element is maddeningly askew. The appearance of impossibility is, however, exactly what makes some puzzles so interesting. They call into play what one puzzle solver has called "a kind of sideways approach to logic that is not reducible to formula"—exactly what Arthur Koestler had in mind when he wrote, in *The Act of Creation*, about the manner in which creative people sometimes find themselves "blocked," unable to see any way to move toward a problem's solution. It is then, he writes, during this "period of incubation," that unexpected insights often come, seemingly out of nowhere.

This process applies equally well to puzzles like the ones in this chapter. Though you cannot always tell exactly where you are headed, or indeed whether you are headed anywhere at all, persistence—no matter how frustrated and seemingly purposeless—will usually yield results.

All the puzzles in this chapter, then, will give way to a properly enlightened persistence, even though that may seem unlikely when you first set eyes on them. They require no knowledge that the ordinary reader does not have. They are utterly free of trickery. There are no misleading clues, nor are there any of the other base forms of skulduggery all too often found in puzzles. Furthermore, you don't need a computer or a wastebasketful of calculations. These are, in short, exactly what they appear to be: tough, rigidly logical problems that can be solved by tough, rigidly logical thinking, properly seasoned every now and then with a bit of the aforementioned sideways approach. Two or three, for comic relief, are really quite easy.

It may be, of course, that you are one of the lucky ones who will have no need to rely on persistence. After all, a single blinding burst of intellect will do nicely, too. But isn't it good to know persistence is there to fall back on if you should need it?

1. Moving Experience

By moving only one pail, line them up so that full pails and empty ones alternate:

2. Horseplay

An aged and, it appears, somewhat eccentric king wants to pass his throne on to one of his two sons. He decrees that a horse race shall be held and that the son who owns the slower horse shall become king. The sons, each fearing that the other will cheat by having his horse go less fast than it is capable of, ask a wise man's advice. With only two words the wise man insures that the race will be fair. What does he say?

3. Troublesome Ten

How are the following numbers arranged? 0, 2, 3, 6, 7, 1, 9, 4, 5, 8.

4. Next

What are the next four numbers in this series: 12, 1, 1, 1, 2, 1, 3 . . . ?

5. Liquid Assets

A wine merchant dies, leaving his three sons seven barrels full of wine, seven barrels half full of wine, and seven empty barrels. In his will he specifies that each son shall receive exactly the same number of full, half-full, and empty barrels. Can his wish be carried out? If so, how?

6. Truth or Consequences

A smart explorer is captured by savages who order him: "Make a statement. If what you say is true, you will be hanged. If it is false, you will be shot." What does the explorer say that saves his life?

7. Cover-up

Water lilies double in area every twenty-four hours. At the beginning of the summer there is one water lily on a lake. It takes sixty days for the lake to become completely covered with water lilies. On what day is it half covered?

8. Ups and Downs

On his way to work each day, a man living on the fifteenth floor of an apartment building takes the elevator to the first floor. On his return, he takes it to the seventh floor and walks the remaining eight floors to his apartment. Why?

9. Double Cross

You want to get to a castle that is surrounded by a ten-foot moat (see diagram). You have two planks, each nine and a half feet long, but nothing to fasten them together with. How can you use the planks to reach the castle?

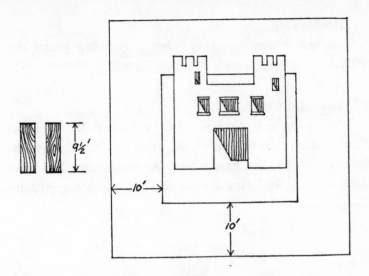

10. Hourglass Figures

You have two hourglasses—a four-minute glass and a seven-minute glass. You want to measure nine minutes. How do you do it?

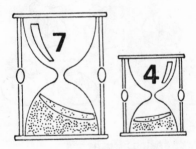

11. The Rules

A certain bus line does not allow passengers to carry luggage over four feet long onto its buses. A man has a five-foot fishing rod. How can he take it onto a bus?

12. Double Play

Two men played checkers. They played five games and each won the same number of games. How?

13. Balancing Act

Ten bags are full of coins. All the coins look the same, but those in one of the bags weigh one gram less than those in the other nine bags. You have a scale but are permitted to make only one weighing. How do you find out which bag contains the lighter coins?

14. The Case of the Jealous Husbands

Three men, traveling with their wives, come to a river. There they find one boat that can hold only two people at a time. Since all the husbands are extremely jealous, no woman can be left with a man unless her husband is present. How do they cross the river?

15. Waiting Game

A man who enjoys watching trains likes to walk to a nearby railroad track to wait for one to go by. Each time, upon his return, he makes a note of whether the one he saw was a passenger train or a freight. Over the years, his figures show that 90 per cent of the trains have been passenger trains. One day he meets an official of the railroad and is surprised to learn that in fact passenger trains and freight trains are precisely equal in number. Why did the man, whom we may presume to have made random trips to the railroad tracks, see such a disproportionate number of passenger trains?

16. Sorting the Numbers

The numbers from 1 to 14 are divided into three groups as follows:

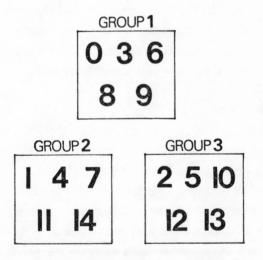

GROUP 1

0 3 6
8 9

GROUP 2

1 4 7
11 14

GROUP 3

2 5 10
12 13

Which groups do the next three numbers belong in?

15 16 17

17. Sleeper

A census taker asks a housewife how many people live in her house and what their ages are. The woman tells him that her three daughters live in the house, that the product of their ages is thirty-six, and that the sum of their ages is the number of the house next door. The census taker goes next door and looks at the number of the house. When he returns he tells the woman that the information she gave him is not sufficient, whereupon the woman tells him, "My oldest daughter is sleeping upstairs." The census taker thanks her and promptly figures out the daughters' ages. What are they and how does he know?

18. Price List

A woman goes into a hardware store to buy something for her house. She asks the clerk the price, and the clerk replies, "The price of one is twelve cents, the price of thirty is twenty-four cents, and the price of a hundred and forty-four is thirty-six cents." What does the woman want to buy?

19. Lucky Numbers

Two men are talking. One says to the other, "I have three sons whose ages I want you to ascertain from the following clues. Stop me when you know their ages.

"1. The sum of their ages is thirteen.

"2. The product of their ages is the same as your age.

"3. My oldest son weighs sixty-one pounds."

"Stop," says the second man. "I know their ages."

What are they?

III

Space, Grand Central Terminal, and the man who stood too close

We have all had the experience of not noticing that the air conditioning in an office building is on until it is suddenly turned off. For exactly the same reason—call it the invisibility of the familiar—we are unaware of countless things that are nonetheless of enormous importance to us. Space is a good example. Psychologists, as we have seen, have long disagreed over exactly how many individually identifiable components there are in a person's I.Q. Is it just one? Is it 120? There is practically no disagreement, however, about the fact that one of those components, no matter what the total may ultimately be determined to be, is the ability to think in spatial terms. A good sense of space is indispensable to doing well on I.Q. tests and, if such tests have any real validity, even to living and thinking successfully.

Yet few people give much thought to space or to how it impinges upon their lives. Architects do, of course. Industrial designers do. Basketball and football players, calculating their moves in millimeters, assuredly do. But most of the rest of us seldom think about it.

A pity, too. Space, as a moment's reflection will reveal, is in fact of transcendent importance in human affairs. How often have you found yourself feeling uncomfortable solely because the space in which you found yourself was ineptly designed? Compare, if you doubt the effects of space on the human spirit, two buildings, both of them designed for virtually the same purpose. On the one hand, consider Grand Central Terminal in New York City. With its towering vaults, broad corridors, and lavish decorative motifs, Grand Central proclaims the importance of the traveler. One cannot be in the station, even in the crush of rush hour, without feeling elevated, enhanced. The person who designed the station plainly felt that important things would take place in it, that important people (you and I) would pass through it. Now think of almost any contemporary airline terminal in almost any city. The airline terminal, by contrast, was built merely to process passengers —to move you through it as fast as possible, and never mind how you happen to feel about what is being done to you. The person who designed it cared about the process, not the people.

Space is not, however, just a matter of aesthetics. It can have quite practical and demonstrable consequences. Some years ago I worked with a South American writer. He was a pleasant, intelligent, and able person. He did his job well. Yet I always felt vaguely uncomfortable with him. Was it an only partly concealed aggressiveness that I sensed in him? Or something else? I did not know, and it was not until some time after he had returned to South America that I finally learned what the problem had been. In his part of the world, two people in conversation customarily stand only a foot and a half or so apart, while in the United States we stand perhaps two feet apart. The difference was enough to make me feel that he was crowding me, and it was no doubt enough to make him feel that I was being remote and standoffish.

To do well on the problems in this chapter will not necessarily help solve social problems like that one. Nor will it win you friends or otherwise improve your life. It may, in fact, do exactly the opposite, particularly if, upon discovering a puzzle you especially like, you force everyone you encounter to try it too (a malady that should perhaps be known as Fixx's syndrome). But at least you will have the satisfaction of knowing, as you work your way through them, that they are based on one of the crucial capacities of your mind.

1. Garden Spot
Plant ten trees in five rows of four trees each.

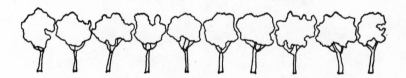

2. Pieces of Eight
Cut a cake into eight equal pieces with only three cuts.

3. Wolf Pen

Nine wolves are in a square enclosure at the zoo. Build two more square enclosures and put each wolf in a pen by itself:

4. Counting Sheep

Sheep, on the other hand, are kept in a circular pen. Draw three lines and put each sheep in a pen by itself:

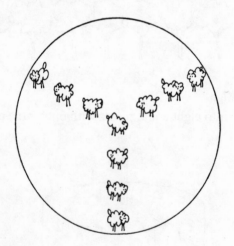

5. Outside Chance

Without lifting your pencil from the paper, join all sixteen dots with six straight lines:

6. Variation on a Variation

The problem above is a variation of the more common nine-dot problem, in which you are asked to connect the dots using four straight lines. Though most people do not at first think of going outside the confines of the dots, the puzzle is actually solved quite easily:

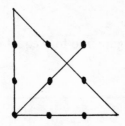

But can you solve it using only *three* straight lines?

7. Knowing the Angles

How many triangles can you find in this figure?

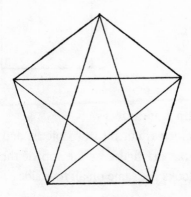

8. Playing the Angles

Divide the figure into four equal parts, each one the same size and shape:

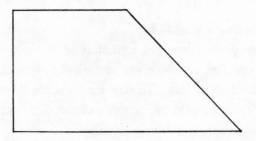

9. Four in One

Now divide this figure into four equal parts of the same size and shape:

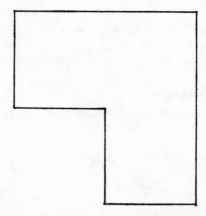

10. Keeping Up Appearances

A wooden block is cut into two pieces and reassembled so that it looks like the figure at the top of the page opposite. (The pattern looks the same on all four sides.) How is it done?

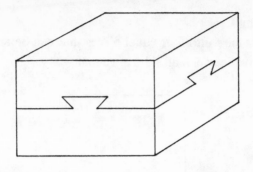

11. Square Deal

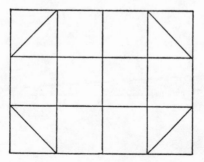

CAN YOU DRAW A PERFECT SQUARE HAVING ONE DOT ON EACH OF ITS 4 SIDES BUT NO SIDE IS TO TOUCH ANY OF THE WORDS WHICH ARE PRINTED HEREIN? IT IS NOT AS EASY AS IT MAY APPEAR AT FIRST GLANCE.

12. Once Over Lightly

Without lifting your pencil from the paper, or folding the paper, make the following figure, going over each line only once:

13. Cutting Up

Cut a square into four equal pieces that can be arranged to form a cross in which all sides are equal.

14. Bugged

Four bugs—A, B, C, and D—are at the corners of a ten-inch square. Simultaneously, and at a constant rate, A crawls directly toward B, B toward C, C toward D, and D toward A. How far does each bug travel before they meet?

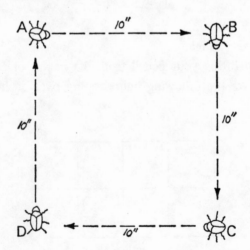

IV

Words for the wise

When I was studying Latin in high school the teacher, Mr. Wedge, one day drew the following picture on the blackboard:

This mysterious object, he explained, had been found by archaeologists excavating the site of an ancient Roman city. What, he asked us, did we think its purpose had been? The entire class began puzzling. The inscription, whatever it was, looked vaguely like Latin, and the object certainly looked ancient enough, but no one could figure it out. Finally, Mr. Wedge showed us how to divide the letters into the proper bunches: TO/TIE/HORSES/TO. An anguished groan went up, and I of course joined in. But that moment was the beginning of a lifelong love affair with verbal puzzles. The ones in this chapter are some of the best I have come across over the years.

1. Categories
The letters of the alphabet can be grouped into four distinct classes: The first thirteen letters establish the categories:
AM
BCDEK
FGJL
HI
Place the remaining thirteen letters in their proper categories.

2. Spooked
What word has five consonants in a row?

3. Invitation
According to E. M. Halliday, an editor of *American Heritage*, Frederick the Great once sent the following message to Voltaire:

$$\frac{6}{100}$$

—and received the following reply:

What did the exchange mean?

4. About December

This is an unusual month—Santa, snow, and so on. This is an unusual paragraph, too. How quickly can you find out what is so uncommon about it? It looks so ordinary that you may think nothing is odd about it until you match it with most paragraphs this long. If you put your mind to it and study it you will find out, but nobody may assist you; do it without any coaching. Go to work and try your skill at figuring it out. Par on it is about half an hour. Good luck—and don't blow your cool.

5. Strange

What five-letter word has only one consonant?

6. Key Question
What word contains six consonants in a row?

7. Fore and Aft
Put the same letters at the front and back of *ergro* to form a common English word.

8. Ups and Downs
What simple English statement is represented by the following?

$$\frac{\text{Stand}}{1} \quad \frac{\text{Take}}{U} \quad \frac{\text{Mine}}{2} \quad \frac{\text{Taking}}{\text{My}}$$

9. Vowel Play
What words contain all six vowels in order? (There are at least two of them.)

10. Repeater
What word contains the same vowel repeated six times?

11. Bad Spellers
It is said that no one in Lord Palmerston's cabinet could spell the following correctly when it was dictated to him: *It is disagreeable to witness the embarrassment of a harassed peddler gauging the symmetry of a peeled potato.* Try it on your friends and see if things have improved since Palmerston's time.

12. Fish Story
Years ago—so long ago that I no longer remember the source (was it Shaw?)—I read, in connection with the

vagaries of English pronunciation, that *ghoti* can be made to spell *fish*—the *f* sound as in *enough, i* as in *women,* and *sh* as in *attention.* What, by similar (but not precisely identical) reasoning, does *iewkngheaurrhphthewempeighghteaps* spell?

13. The Long Way

What one-syllable word has nine letters?

14. Less Is More

What one-syllable word, when two letters are removed from it, becomes a two-syllable word?

15. Formula

What common chemical compound is represented by the following: HIJKLMNO?

16. Reckoning

Make a sentence by rearranging the following:

17. Inside Stories

What English words contain the following letters consecutively and in the order given?

wsst	*wkw*
ycam	*cheo*
bpoe	*erha*
simmo	*gnt*

V

Mathematics, misery,
and pure joy

Think back to your first encounter with numbers, to your earliest days of struggling with arithmetic. Do you find your mind filled with happy memories of the experience? If your school days were anything like mine, you do not. On the contrary, chances are that what you remember are hour after childhood hour of grinding travail—unendingly pointless calculations, vast tables that needed to be memorized, frustrating efforts to get an answer to come out right. Even on a first meeting, one might actually find oneself enjoying reading or geography or history. But practically no child likes arithmetic.

This is a curious phenomenon, one full of ironies, since it so frequently happens that at some time in the ensuing years mathematics turns into the purest and most joyful of recreations. ("Pick a number from one to ten . . .") On the table at my side as I write this are several books: Martin Gardner's wonderful *Mathematical Carnival,* Jack Frohlichstein's *Mathematical Fun, Games and Puzzles,* Geoffrey Mott-Smith's *Mathematical Puzzles, The Calculator Handbook,* by A. N. Feldzamen and Faye Henle, and Philip Heafford's *The Math*

Entertainer. All of them—even the calculator guide, with its chapter on "Hobbies, Recreations, and Gambling"—dwell, you will notice, on the pleasures of mathematics. They all seem to be saying: At times we *must* use math; these books are for those carefree times when we simply *want to.*

The recreational uses of math are by no means new. Martin Gardner writes of an occurrence a century and a half ago in the little town of Cabot, in the northeastern corner of Vermont. Today Cabot is known chiefly for the cheeses produced at its dairy co-operative, but in the early years of the nineteenth century it was celebrated as the home of one Zerah Colburn, a calculating prodigy who, even before he could read and write, had learned the multiplication table to 100. Young Zerah performed publicly in England when he was eight years old, multiplying two four-digit numbers nearly as fast as any calculator can today, and he even wrote an autobiography, *A Memoir of Zerah Colburn: written by himself . . . with his peculiar methods of calculation.* His audiences were so impressed that several admirers, including Washington Irving, raised money to send him to school in London and Paris.

Nor was Zerah Colburn by any means the first person to think of entertaining us with mathematics. Mathematical puzzles, games, and paradoxes can be traced back to the very brink of prehistory. This is really not very surprising. We take it for granted, just as soon as teachers stop rubbing our noses in numbers, that math can be wonderful fun. It is in that spirit that the puzzles in this chapter are offered. Regard them not as enemies to be swiftly bludgeoned and conquered, but as friendly companions to spend a few convivial hours with. They are certain to repay your good will.

1. Double Trouble

Arrange the numerals 1 through 9 so that, when added, they will equal 100.

2. Missing Links

Find the product of the following: $(x-a)(x-b)(x-c)$ . . . $(x-z)$

3. Growing Old Together

A ship is twice as old as its boiler was when the ship was as old as the boiler is. The sum of their ages equals 49 years. How old is the ship and how old is the boiler?

4. Rope Trick

Two flagpoles are each 100 feet high. A rope 150 feet long is strung between the tops of the flagpoles. At its lowest point the rope sags to within 25 feet of the ground. How far apart are the flagpoles?

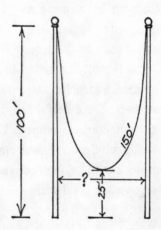

5. Animal Farm

A farmer buys 100 animals for $100. Cows are $10 each, sheep $3.00 each, and pigs 50 cents each. (Plainly, this all happened quite some time ago.) How many of each did he buy?

6. Changeless

What is the largest sum of money in current United States coins (but no silver dollars, please) that a person can have in his pocket without being able to give someone change for a dollar, half dollar, quarter, dime, or nickel?

7. The Missing Dollar

This is an old but wonderfully perplexing problem.

Three men went to a hotel and were told that there was only one room left and that it would cost $30 for the night. They paid $10 apiece and went to the room. The desk clerk, discovering that by mistake he had overcharged them by $5.00, asked the bellboy to return the $5.00. The bellboy, not being as honest as the desk clerk, reasoned that since $5.00 is not easy to divide three ways, he would keep $2.00 and return $1.00 to each of the three men. Each man thus actually paid only $9.00 apiece, or a total of $27 for the room. Add to that the $2.00 the bellboy kept, and the total is $29. Where did the missing dollar go?

8. The Hard Way

Without changing the order of these digits, place the fewest possible mathematical symbols between them in order to make the equation true: 1 2 3 4 5 6 7 8 9=100. It can, of course, be done quite easily by using a "not equals" sign ($\neq$), but that would be taking the easy way out, wouldn't it?

9. Where There's a Will

A Middle Eastern potentate died, leaving 17 camels. His will specified that they be divided among his three sons as follows:

½ to the oldest son

⅓ to the second son

⅑ to the youngest son

The three sons were puzzling over how this could be done when a wise man happened to ride by on a camel. How did the wise man solve their problem?

10. X Marks the Spot

Solve for X:

$$\sqrt{X+\sqrt{X+\sqrt{X.....}}} = 2$$

11. Time Out

A customer gives a $20 bill to a jeweler for a watch priced at $12. Because he is short of change, the jeweler changes the $20 bill at a store next door. He gives the watch and $8.00 to the customer. Later the neighboring storekeeper, discovering the $20 bill to be counterfeit, returns it to the jeweler, who exchanges it for a genuine $20 bill. If the jeweler had a 100 per cent markup on the watch, how much did he actually lose in the transaction?

12. Burned Up

How many cigars can a hobo make from twenty-five cigar butts if he needs five butts to make one cigar?

13. Up a Tree

If John gives Paul one apple, they will have the same number of apples. If Paul gives John one, John will have twice as many as Paul has. How many apples does each have?

14. It All Adds Up

Arrange eight 8s so that when added they will equal 1,000.

15. Line-up

By drawing one line, make the following figure into an even number (without violating numerical convention):

VI

Disturbers of
the puzzler's peace

Lest I be suspected of a penchant for underhandedness that I do not, so far as I know, even remotely possess, let me say at once that, of all the chapters in this book, this is the one I like least. (It is not without significance that it is among the shortest.) In my earliest ruminations, in fact, I did not even plan to include it, not through oversight but because the sorts of puzzles found here seem to me uncomfortably close to shaggy-dog stories, to be greeted not with appreciation but with groans.

There are, I know, plenty of people who dearly love puzzles that inflict an intellectual whiplash. My daughter Betsy, thirteen years old and not at all reluctant to outwit her elders when she can, is an excellent example. I had long ago encountered, as you no doubt have, the familiar bus driver puzzle. It goes: "You're driving a bus. At the first stop two passengers get on. At the next, seven passengers get on and one gets off . . ." and so on through a dozen or more stops, until you are ultimately flattened by the disarming question: "How many times did the bus stop?" So I was ready, or at least thought I was, when Betsy began to recite the comings and goings of the bus passengers—ready, indeed, for anything, for I was cannily counting both the stops *and* the passengers. But what I was not ready for, as Betsy was pretty sure I would not be, was what turned out to be her question, "How old was the bus driver?" (Nor was I able, by that time, to remember that she had begun by saying, *"You're* driving a bus . . .")

Despite such firsthand evidence of the popularity of this kind of puzzle, I nonetheless did not, as I say, intend to include any in this book. Its predecessor, *Games for the Superintelligent,* gained whatever freedom from impurity it had from the fact that its puzzles, despite their other flaws and shortcomings, were all impeccably straightforward and could be solved, each and every one of them, by nothing trickier than a rigorous application of logic. You didn't have to wonder if the author was trying to outwit you—he wasn't—and readers, to judge by the evidence that reached me, welcomed the certainty that what they had to deal with were merely the puzzles themselves and not a syntactical mine field.

All this sounds, four years after the fact, impressively far-sighted. In truth it was nothing of the sort. I simply included the kinds of puzzles that give me special delight, and it was only luck that there proved to be a lot of other people who like the same kind of puzzle. Nevertheless, as I talked with puzzle aficionados I became increasingly aware that there are plenty of them who are not the least bit like me: they genuinely like—nay, *crave*—tricks, the trickier the better. Then, as I went through my files in preparation for compiling this book, I was struck by how many people—scores of them, in fact—had sent me puzzles that deliberately set out to deceive. I was also struck, though it took me a long time to admit it, even to myself, by the fact that despite my better instincts I found some of them wonderfully amusing.

And so it was that I determined to include a sampling in this volume. My first thought was to seed them subversively through the entire book, popping them in at odd, unsuspected moments like tacks in a driveway. But that would have rendered all the puzzles suspect. A reader would never have been able to tell whether he was faced with a genuine puzzle or some bit of sleight of hand. No, it was better, even at the risk of giving too obvious a warning blast, to banish the whiplash puzzles to their own preserve, like so many dangerous animals. And that is precisely what, for better or worse, this chapter is all about.

1. Where There's Smoke

If you had only one match and entered a room in which there were a kerosene lamp, a fireplace, and a wood-burning stove, which should you light first?

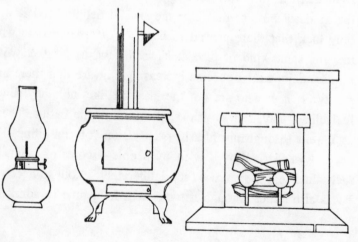

2. Last Wrongs

Can a man living in Chapel Hill, North Carolina, be buried west of the Mississippi?

3. Look Again

There is three errers in this sentence. Can you find them?

4. Coin Trick

You have thirty-five cents in two coins. One of them is not a quarter. What are the coins?

5. Over and Out

Construct this figure without lifting your pencil from the surface of the paper and without traversing any line more than once:

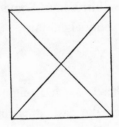

6. So You Think You Know the Law

Is it legal in South Dakota for a man to marry his widow's sister?

7. Holiday

Do they have a Fourth of July in England?

8. Disaster

If a plane crashes directly on the line between two states, where are the survivors buried?

9. Voyager

How many animals of each species did Moses take aboard the ark with him?

10. Kaffeeklatsch

You have three cups of coffee and fourteen lumps of sugar. Sweeten all three cups using an odd number of lumps in each one. (You must use all the lumps.)

11. Days Off

Some months have thirty days. Some have thirty-one. How many months have twenty-eight days?

12. Cannonball

An electric train heads north at eighty miles an hour. The wind is blowing from the east at twenty miles an hour. In what direction will the smoke from the engine point?

13. In the Groove

How many grooves does the average twelve-inch 33⅓ LP record have?

VII

Solving puzzles
the superintelligent way

As we saw in Chapter I, the minds of bright people are significantly different—in as many as 120 ways, some say— from those of their less intelligent brethren. This is as true in solving puzzles as it is in trying to live a rational life. While the ordinary mind is likely to be stubbornly trying a single fruitless assault on a problem, the gifted mind is quickly sweeping through a range of choices and winnowing the most promising methods from the many that occur to it. Then, if those methods fail, rather than giving up in discouragement it moves on to what at first seemed the less likely routes, until at length it arrives at a solution.

It is exactly as if the bright person were a miniature think tank. Instead, however, of being free to assign a separate task force to each aspect of a problem, as Herman Kahn or the Pentagon can, there is only one person to assign to all aspects. And instead of being able to study every facet of a problem simultaneously, the bright person must study them one at a time. This method is a lot slower, but it often works just as well. The chief reason for its success is that the bright person is likely to be relatively indefatigable. (Remember one of Sir Francis Galton's components of intelligence: "power of work.") While the less intelligent person, unsure of ever being able to solve a problem at all, is easily discouraged, the intelligent person is fairly sure of succeeding and therefore presses on, discouragements be damned.

Because the difference between the two types of mind depends so much upon their differing power of work, it is often difficult if not impossible to demonstrate in detail how the action of one differs from that of the other. It is, moreover, obvious that many of the things that only exceptionally intelligent minds can *do* can be readily *understood* by considerably less intelligent minds. We do not have to be geniuses ourselves to appreciate Shakespeare or understand Newton's laws of motion. It is, in fact, uncommon for someone to make so spectacularly brilliant an intellectual leap that we can only stand in awe. Most of the time we can, if we wish, tell ourselves: Why, I could easily have done that if it had only occurred to me to! (We do not dwell on the fact that it simply did *not* occur to us to.)

Despite the difficulty of showing, clearly and without ambiguity, the characteristic ways in which bright people solve problems, their methods can at least be suggested by pointing to specific examples. To this end, let us dissect in some detail a few of the puzzles in this book.

Chapter II, Puzzle 3: At first glance this question seems to be based on a quite ordinary series of numbers, 0, 2, 3, 6, 7, 1, 9, 4, 5, 8. The series is much like the ones we have encountered all our lives. For this reason the solver, no matter what his intelligence, will most likely start by treating it in the customary way. He will examine the intervals between numbers, check to see whether any patterns repeat themselves, and, as those attempts fail, make other efforts of increasing complexity. At this point, all his efforts having come to nothing, the person of ordinary intelligence may well feel the first twinges of discouragement. Does solving the puzzle rely, perhaps, on some mathematical technique or formula he does not know? The superintelligent solver, by contrast, has a secret weapon: he knows that the puzzle, by virtue of being in this book, is likely to have a bit of English on it. He therefore veers sharply, abandons the fairly unimaginative course he has been following (with, however, the idea that he may have to return to it later), and begins looking for some totally different line of attack. Now, although he does not yet know it, he is on the right track at last. He decides, experimentally, to treat the numbers not as numbers at all but as objects. What about their shapes—their curves, straight lines, combination of curves and straight lines, and so forth? No solution presenting itself, he moves on. What about treating the numbers as words—*zero, two, three, six, seven* . . . etc.? He counts their letters, checks them for patterns, repetitions. Finding nothing there, he moves, finally, to the first letters of the words: *z, t, t, s, s, o, n, f, f, e.* Before he even has the ten letters down on paper, that *z* gives it all away: The numbers are, of course, in reverse alphabetical order.

Principle 1: Consider the context of a puzzle first.

Chapter II, Puzzle 10: You are asked to use two hourglasses, a four-minute glass and a seven-minute glass, to measure out nine minutes. It requires only a moment's reflection to realize that seven and four, no matter how they may be

157

arranged, cannot be made to add up to nine. Where, then, do we go from here? The person of ordinary intelligence is unlikely to go much of anywhere. Or perhaps he gets a bit further when an analogy occurs to him: he thinks of those puzzles about cooks who want to measure a certain amount of, say, sugar but have measuring cups of the wrong size. This line of speculation leads to a dead end, for time as measured by hourglasses cannot be subtracted in the way sugar in a measuring cup can. Time flows on and is gone; one cannot (alas!) return to some previous time, as one can pour out a bit of sugar and thereby have less. It is at this point that the superintelligent person decides to try something else. But what else is there to try? An hourglass is either running or it is not running, and no combination of running and stopped hourglasses can possibly yield nine minutes. Or can it? What about stopping one of the hourglasses in mid-run and then, if need be, restarting it? With that insight, the solution is close at hand. The solver's whole difficulty, incidentally, arises from the assumption that sand in an hourglass must be allowed to run all the way through. That, of course, is what usually happens, but there is no law saying it must always happen that way.

Principle 2: Look for uncommon ways of using a puzzle's components.

Chapter II, Puzzle 19: This is one of my favorite puzzles. A reader sent it to me in a letter, and something about his tone impressed and reassured me. I felt certain he wasn't trying to trick me but that the puzzle was honest and would reward my efforts. It did. I worked it in two sessions, the first a brief one of terrible frustration in which I was especially puzzled by the seeming irrelevance of the son's weight and by the fact, with respect to Clue No. 2, that I didn't *know* what the man's age was. How could an answer possibly be put together from such meager information? I was helpless. I stopped, went outdoors, pruned a rosebush or two. When I came back to the puzzle I had fresh determination. Suddenly it occurred to me that the weight might well be irrelevant and that the clue must be telling me something else—that there is only one oldest son, not two of the same age. It then occurred to me that it might be worth while to jot down the various combinations of ages that could satisfy the problem, so I started: 11, 1, 1; 10, 1, 2 . . . and so forth. There were fourteen of them. A moment's study revealed that two of the combinations yielded the same product: 36. Here, then, was the solution! If the answer were not one of the combinations that yield 36, the man would have known the correct combination after hearing Clue No. 2. The fact that he did not demonstrates that there was still a question in his mind, a question that was finally resolved with Clue No. 3. There is another little secret to solving this puzzle, and if it had occurred to me earlier I could have worked it in a tenth the time: the fact that you and I don't know the man's age doesn't mean that *he* doesn't know it. Of course he knows it, and that is the key to solving this puzzle.

Principle 3: If logic and persistence don't yield an answer, go out and smell the roses for a while.

Chapter III, Puzzle 1: At first glance it appears that this puzzle is simply impossible to solve. Five rows of four trees each adds up, after all, to twenty trees, or so it appears. Even allowing for the use of a few trees in more than one row, it seems exceedingly unlikely that the number of trees required can be reduced to a mere ten. Then, however, the principle becomes clear: it is necessary to plant the trees as densely as possible, making each tree serve in as many rows as possible. Diagram after diagram is tried; none works—not at first anyway. But then, sooner or later, the wondrous symmetry of nature and mathematics asserts itself and there it is, that simple and elegant answer: a star.

Principle 4: Keep at it.

Chapter III, Puzzle 2: You are asked to cut a cake into eight equal pieces with only three cuts. Any three cuts made vertically will, it is apparent, yield six pieces at most. Two cuts made vertically and a third cut made along a radius will yield only five pieces. Three cuts that fail to intersect will yield only four pieces. Things seem to be getting not better but worse! At this point the person of ordinary intelligence is likely to imagine that he is faced with something as clearly impossible as trying to separate two interlocking rings; mathematically, it simply can't be done. But it is precisely here that the superintelligent puzzle solver begins to rise to the challenge. He looks first at the components of the puzzle: (1) a cake and (2) a knife for cutting it into those elusive eight pieces. He reminds himself that the puzzle can, after all, be solved; it would not be in this book if it could not (see Principle 1 above). Furthermore, he knows there is nothing tricky or misleading about the question. (He has been assured that all the tricky questions have been sequestered in Chapter VI.) So he knows it is worth his while to treat the puzzle in a straightforward way—he need not suspect an ambush. He is, at the same time, certain by now that it cannot be solved by making three cuts of the kind we customarily make in cakes. Well, what other kinds are there? A rough sort of answer comes to him at once: vertical cuts, horizontal cuts, cuts taking various improbable directions through the cake. It is a matter of only a few moments before he sees that two vertical cuts, at right angles to each other, and one horizontal cut will do the trick neatly.

Principle 5: If something has always been done one way, look for another way.

Chapter III, Puzzle 5: In this one you are asked to join sixteen dots with six straight lines without lifting your pencil from the paper. Any puzzler, no matter what his intelligence, will no doubt find a pencil and start fiddling. (It always makes sense to get a quick view of the magnitude of things.) In a short time it will be clear that this one isn't going to be easy; there always seem to be too many dots and too few lines. If you are knowledgeable about puzzles, you will recall that in some problems of this general type the solution can be reached only by resorting to extraordinary measures—folding the paper, for example, or piercing it with a pencil point and letting a line snake its way through the hole from one side to the other. But there is nothing in the language of this puzzle to suggest that such lawbreaking is called for. Furthermore, solutions based on such methods would unquestionably constitute trickery, wouldn't they? (There will be time enough later, if things start to go really badly, to ask if we are being tricked.) For the time being, better to treat it as a straightforward question, neither more nor less complex than it seems to be. What, therefore, can we do that we aren't now doing? Practically anyone, regardless of his intelligence, will no doubt stumble onto the answer sooner or later, but the superintelligent, having got this far, will probably find it almost immediately. (Mental quickness, psychologists agree, is an important component of brightness.) The reason is that it will probably occur to him to ask himself whether he is by chance working under some unnecessary restriction. Of course he is—no one told him that he had to stay within the imaginary boundary of the square created by the sixteen dots!

Principle 6: Work only within those restrictions that are explicitly stated. All others are irrelevant.

Chapter IV, Puzzle 1: This puzzle is both difficult and simple. The difficulty arises from the fact that we are thoroughly conditioned to think of letters as *letters* and not as objects. *A,* for example, is the first letter of the alphabet. It is a vowel, too. Those things are uppermost in our minds. Only rarely do we think of *A* as a shape, pointed at the top like, appropriately enough, an A-frame house, with a supporting girder running horizontally to keep it from spreading out and collapsing in a most unvowellike heap. Once we have managed to bring ourselves to look at *A* (and at the other letters) in that way, the rest is easy.

Principle 7: Don't get tripped up by unexpressed hypotheses. Examine all the alternatives.

Chapter V, Puzzle 2: To find the product of the series $(x-a)(x-b)(x-c)$ . . . $(x-z)$ appears to be, as anyone can instantly see, a problem of unusual complexity for a book like this. The first reaction of the intelligent puzzle solver is therefore surprise. What is a puzzle like that doing here? It cannot even be solved with the use of a pocket calculator—not, anyway, by any method known to a mathematical layman. More and more, as one looks at it, it begins to look like something you might find on a blackboard at the Institute for Advanced Studies, being studied by a committee of bearded mathematicians, their brows furrowed in puzzlement. At this point, the intelligent solver may begin to suspect that only one reaction is really appropriate: laughter. It is, after all, ridiculous to suppose that a problem as difficult as all that would be in this book. But what to do about it? It is one thing to know that one's leg is being pulled and quite another to find out who or what is pulling it. Where, exactly, is the clue to the mystery? Well, perhaps we are making some assumption that we ought not to make (see Principle 4). What about that ellipsis (. . .), that unobtrusive mathematical symbol for *et cetera?* Ever since we first studied algebra in school, we have been seeing and using those harmless little dots; never have they concealed anything more surprising than an orderly and continuous series. What, however, lies within these particular three dots? Now, at last, we are on the track. As we start working our way through the unexpressed elements of the equation—$(x-d)$, $(x-e)$, and so forth—it occurs to us that eventually we will come to $(x-x)$. Because $(x-x)$ equals zero, the rest of the equation, no matter how tangled and mathematically variegated it is, will of course equal zero!

Principle 8: If you can't find the solution by looking at the forest, look at the trees.

Chapter V, Puzzle 5: This puzzle is difficult only if the flagpoles are not right together. If they are, as we have seen, it is absurdly simple. An extremely bright person, noticing this, decides to take a moment to see if, by chance, they *are* right together. If they are not, only a few moments have been lost. If they are, much has been gained. The bright person is not afraid to digress, to risk a small loss for a potentially large gain.

Principle 9: When you're watching a magician, don't concentrate only on the rabbit. Something important may be going on somewhere else.

Chapter V, Puzzle 16: You are given the Roman numerals representing 9—that is, IX—and asked to change them into an even number between five and ten by adding only one line. The problem appears to have no solution. One line, after all, is simply I, and that gets us nowhere. Aha! But no one said it had to be a straight line. Could the line possibly be a bent one —V? That could give us VIX, or four, but four does not qualify since it is not between five and ten. (It could also give us IVX, or six, but the unconventional notation rules out that solution.) There seems, then, to be no way to solve this one, so long as we treat IX as Roman numerals. What else could they be, then? Well, for one thing, as the superintelligent person quickly sees, they could be treated simply as ordinary letters—a capital *i* and a capital *x*. What single line, added to *i* and *x*, might turn those letters into a word representing an even number between five and ten? From here on it's all downhill: simply note what letters of the alphabet can be formed with a single line—it is surprising how many there are —and try adding them to *i* and *x*. It will not be long before *six* turns up.

Principle 10: Assume that nothing is what it seems to be.

Now, armed with this ten-point puzzle-solving arsenal, go back to Chapters II through VII and try some of the questions you found too tough the first time through.

See? Aren't you doing better already?

VIII

Rating your intelligence

Let us suppose that thus far in your life you have been a mere dabbler in matters superintelligent. Now you would like to become a certified member of the superintelligentsia. There are many methods. Only one of them, however, has genuine style, and that is to think your way into Mensa, the international society for people with extraordinarily high I.Q.s To qualify for membership, you need an I.Q. in the top 2 per cent of the population. That's 133 on the Stanford-Binet test, 130 on the Wechsler Adult test, a combined score of 1,300 on the College Entrance Examination Board aptitude tests, 140 on the Army General Classification Test, and 70 on the Navy General Classification Test. Once a member, you're able to attend meetings (Mensa has more than 125 chapters in the United States and a good many abroad, particularly in England and Canada), join groups with special interests ranging from parapsychology to gourmet cooking, serve as a subject in psychological studies, and participate in some of the headiest conversation to be found anywhere.

What are a person's chances of qualifying? Not as remote as you might think, especially for anyone reading this book. Two per cent works out, after all, to one in every fifty people, so a good many of those you run into each day could become members if they wanted to. And if, by chance, you spend a lot of time with people who work with their brains (college professors, let's say, or engineers or lawyers or doctors), then the proportion is no doubt considerably higher.

To help determine the likelihood of your being Mensa material yourself, the organization's psychologist, Max L. Fogel, has prepared a special test. It is published here for the first time.

The instructions are simple: Work as hard as you can for no more than forty-five minutes, then stop. A key for scoring appears on page 101. If you finish in less than forty minutes, give yourself a one-point bonus; in less than thirty-five minutes, a two-point bonus; in less than thirty minutes, a three-point bonus.

Now, get your watch and pencils ready.

All set?

Turn the page and begin.

1. Which figure in the bottom row should appear next in the top row?

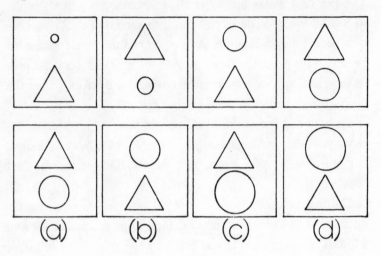

(a)   (b)   (c)   (d)

2. Which figure in the bottom row should appear next in the top row?

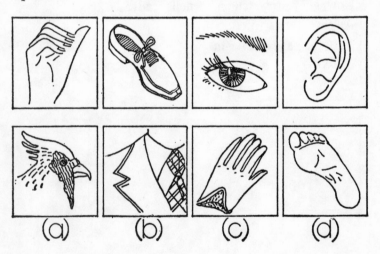

(a)   (b)   (c)   (d)

3. Which figure in the bottom row should appear next in the top row?

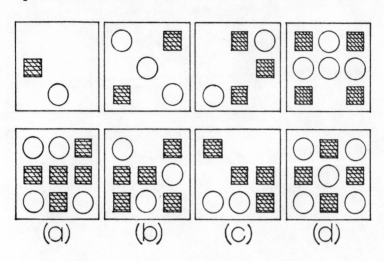

4. Which figure in the bottom row should appear next in the top row?

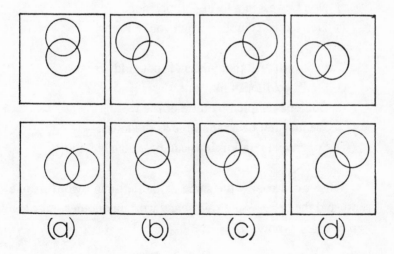

5. Which figure in the bottom row should appear next in the top row?

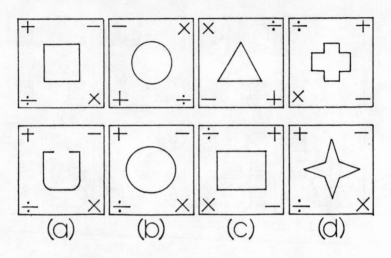

(a) (b) (c) (d)

6. "Don't throw good money after bad" means:
 (a) Take your loss and walk away from it.
 (b) Don't gamble; think of the future.
 (c) Don't invest in a losing proposition.
 (d) Don't keep gambling when you're losing.

7. The proverb "All that glisters is not gold" means:
 (a) Fool's gold looks like gold.
 (b) Don't be tempted by false praise.
 (c) She may not be as adorable as she looks.
 (d) Superficial relationships can be enjoyable, too.

8. What word means the same as the left-hand word in one sense and the same as the right-hand word in another sense?
    pay _____ bottom

9. Love is to _____ as sex is to _____.

(*a*) woman; man

(*b*) cherish; caress

(*c*) enjoy; tolerate

(*d*) obey; liberate

10. What number comes next in the following series?

9, 12, 21, 48

(*a*) 69; (*b*) 70; (*c*) 129; (*d*) 144

11. Most readers of this book are sexy. All readers of this book are superintelligent. Therefore:

(*a*) Sexy readers of this book are also superintelligent.

(*b*) Sex and superintelligence don't mix well.

(*c*) All superintelligent readers of this book are sexy.

(*d*) Most readers of this book are superintelligent about sex.

12. Statistics indicate that men drivers are involved in more accidents than women drivers. It may be concluded that:

(*a*) As usual, male chauvinists are wrong about women's abilities.

(*b*) Men are actually better drivers but drive more frequently.

(*c*) Men and women drive equally well but men log more total mileage.

(*d*) Most truck drivers are men.

(*e*) Sufficient information is not available to justify a conclusion.

171

13. Which country does not belong:

(*a*) Canada;   (*b*) Czechoslovakia;   (*c*) Chile;   (*d*) Iran;
(*e*) Mexico;   (*f*) Rumania;   (*g*) the Soviet Union;   (*h*) the
United States;   (*i*) Venezuela

14. Which word does not belong?

(*a*) bourbon;   (*b*) Burgundy;   (*c*) Chablis;   (*d*) port;
(*e*) sherry;   (*f*) zinfandel

15. The floor space of a large restaurant is divided into four
main dining areas. Half of the main dining areas contain two
smaller dining rooms each and the other half contain four
smaller dining rooms each. Ten diners can be served in each
of half of the total number of rooms; fifteen can be served in
each of the remaining half. What is the maximum number of
diners that can be served at the same time?

(*a*) 100;   (*b*) 125;   (*c*) 150;   (*d*) 175

16.

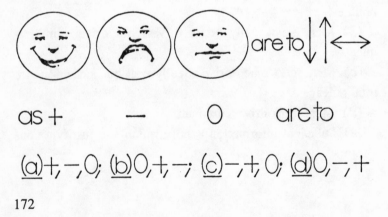

17. How many squares are shown below? (You may ignore any lines that pass through a square.)

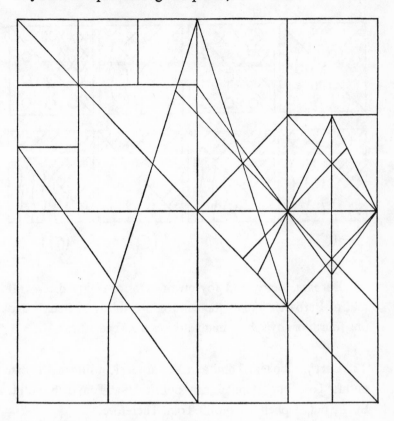

(*a*) 19; (*b*) 20; (*c*) 21; (*d*) 22; (*e*) 23

18. A horse is most like a:
(*a*) camel; (*b*) car; (*c*) cow; (*d*) dog; (*e*) motorcycle

19. F is to L as B is to:
(*a*) D; (*b*) G; (*c*) M; (*d*) T

20. Which figure in the bottom row should appear next in the top row?

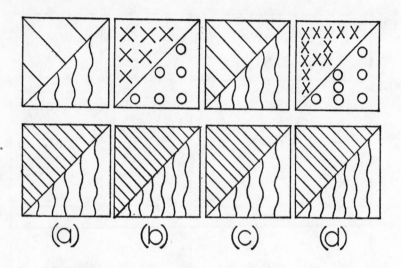

(a)   (b)   (c)   (d)

21. Barbara, Betty, and Joy own a total of eighty dresses. If half of Barbara's equals the sum of two thirds of Betty's and one fourth of Joy's, how many dresses does each own?

22. Bucky, Stephen, Tom, and Vic are weight lifters. Vic can outlift Tom but Stephen can outlift Vic. Tom can outlift Bucky but Stephen can outlift Tom. Therefore:

(*a*) Both Bucky and Stephen can outlift Vic.

(*b*) Vic can outlift Bucky but can't outlift Tom.

(*c*) Vic can outlift Bucky by more than he can outlift Tom.

(*d*) None of the above.

23. If an airplane travels at an average speed of 500 miles per hour, how long will it take to complete twenty trips, of which five are for 1,000 miles, five for 1,500 miles, five for 2,000 miles, and five for 3,000 miles?

(*a*) 2 days and 18 hours

(*b*) 2 days and 21 hours

(*c*) 3 days

(*d*) 3 days and 3 hours

24. What number comes next in the following series?

9, 5, 8, 14, 10, 13

(*a*) 7;   (*b*) 9;   (*c*) 16;   (*d*) 19;   (*e*) 23

25. If $A \times B = 24$, $C \times D = 32$, $B \times D = 48$, and $B \times C = 24$, what does $A \times B \times C \times D$ equal?

(*a*) 480;   (*b*) 576;   (*c*) 744;   (*d*) 768;   (*e*) 824

More helpers

In the nature of things, any collection of mental recreations must be a collaborative effort. A good many of the puzzles and games in this book have been making the rounds for years, occasionally surfacing in print but often simply passing informally from hand to hand when puzzle lovers meet. For this reason there is nowhere the author of a book like this can go to do his research, no library or central repository of what he is looking for. He must depend almost entirely on the help and generosity of others who share his enthusiasms.

In this respect I have been lucky. Over the past several years scores of correspondents have written to me about puzzles. Some of the puzzles have been new to me, while others have been old ones that I might easily have overlooked had I not been reminded of them. In addition, friends, colleagues, and even a few chance acquaintances have offered ideas and given encouragement when it counted.

Among the various partners in this enterprise are:

Nasim Ahmed, Janice N. Anderson, Martin Antila, Rito Avalos, Frances H. Bentley, Stephen Bepko, Gila Berkowitz, Henry M.

Black, Richard M. Block, Ron E. Breland, Maxey Brooke, Bruce Brown, Virginia H. Burney, Mike Buttke, S. Chandrashekara, Kuang-Yeh Chang, Inge Denny, Richard J. Deye, Don Dolezalek, Joseph Drago, Patricia Driskill, Neil E. Duncliffe, Charles W. Dunn, Donald W. Eckrich, Jon Erickson, Clifford J. Falk, Harry Famely, Chris Fisher, Ellen M. Fitzgerald, Max L. Fogel, Donald R. Fosnacht, Richard Gardiner, Jonathan Gerson, Todd Glasford, Jitendra Singh Goela, Anil Goyal, Dale Green, Martin B. Green, Jonathan Groner, Barbara C. Heller, William H. Hernandez, Wolfgang S. Homburger, Pyke Johnson, Jr., Martin J. Kelinsky, Frederick F. Kleinman, Marshall Kurtz, Bruce Kutner, Peter J. Lardieri, Barbara Holtz Levine, Bernard Lewis, Dave Lewis, Geraldine McDaniel, Barbara McKenzie, Raymond J. Martin, Jr., Ann Meadow, Jeffrey R. Miller, John D. Miller, Nancy A. Mitchell, Karen Montgomery, Russell A. Nahigian, Bob Nathan, C. A. Nicolaides, Gary A. Nielsen, Robert F. Oldani, Francis P. Pandolfi, Chris Peters, Joe Poindexter, Edward Purcell, Cal L. Raup, Alvin Reinstein, Steve Ross, T. M. Rostker, D. P. Rougon, Tom Saile, Wolfgang Sannwald, Lee W. Sauer, Jeffry N. Savitz, Ivan Schuller, W. R. Sears, Nicholas Sellers, Fred U. Senfert, Manu Seth, Zach Sklar, Nguyen Thao, Don W. Tope, Elliott J. Tuckel, Jay Valancy, J. A. Washam, Joel R. Weiss, Charles Weissglass, Steve Whipple, C. A. Wiken, Larry Wizenberg, Catherine Woytko, L. Y. Wu, and, as always, the little old lady on Rose Street.

Answers to puzzles

CHAPTER II

1. Pour pail No. 2 into pail No. 5.

1   2   3   4   5   6

2. "Switch horses."

3. In reverse alphabetical order.

4. 1, 4, 1, 5, etc. The numbers represent the chimes of a clock that strikes once on the half hour.

5. Yes. Pour four of the half-full barrels together to make two more full ones. Now there are nine full barrels, three half-full barrels, and nine empty barrels. All can be divided by three.

6. He says, "I will be shot." If this were true, he would, under the terms of his sentence, be hanged. That would be contradictory. If it were false he would be shot—also contradictory. The savages are forced to release the explorer. (So he hopes, anyhow.)

7. The fifty-ninth day.

8. He is a midget and can't reach higher than the seventh-floor button.

9. Simply lay one of the planks diagonally across the edge and the other from that plank to the castle:

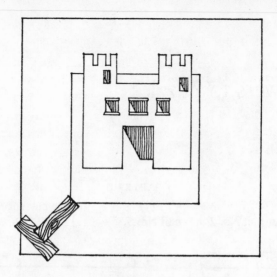

10. Start both hourglasses. When the four-minute glass runs out, turn it over (four minutes elapsed). When the seven-minute glass runs out, turn it over (seven minutes elapsed). When the four-minute glass runs out this time (eight minutes elapsed), the seven-minute glass has been running for one minute. Turn it over once again. When it stops, nine minutes have elapsed.

11. Make a package as shown:

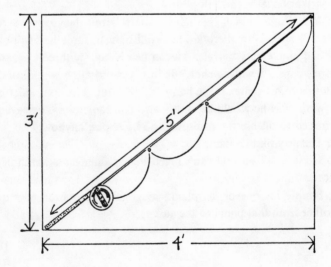

12. They weren't playing each other.

13. Number the bags from 1 to 10. Take from each bag a number of coins equal to the number of the bag—one coin from bag No. 1, two from bag No. 2, and so forth. Weigh them all together. The result will be light by a number of grams equal to the number of the bag that contains the light coins.

14. A and his wife cross. A returns. B's and C's wives cross. A's returns. B and C cross. B and his wife return. A and B cross. C's wife returns. A's and B's wives cross. C returns. C and his wife cross.

15. The freight trains came six minutes after the passenger trains. Thus the man's odds of arriving after a freight and before a passenger train are 9 to 1, since for fifty-four out of every sixty minutes it is a passenger train that is expected.

16. The numbers 15, 16, and 17 should be placed in groups 3, 3, and 2, respectively. Group 1 consists of numbers composed entirely of curved lines, Group 2 consists of numbers composed entirely of straight lines, and Group 3 consists of numbers composed of a combination of curved and straight lines.

17. The woman has a nine-year-old daughter and two-year-old twins. Since the census taker knew both the product and the sum of their ages, confusion could arise only if two or more sets of ages led to the same product and sum. If we break 36 into three factors we find that only two sets of ages (9, 2, 2 and 6, 6, 1) lead to the same sum, 13. The woman's final piece of information tells the census taker that there is only one oldest daughter, not two the same age.

18. House numbers.

19. Nine, two, and two. There are only fourteen combinations of ages that correspond with clues 1 and 2. Since the man solving the puzzle may be presumed to know his own age, the fact that the second clue isn't sufficient to solve the problem shows that his age must be 36—the only product to occur twice. The final clue—that there is only one oldest son, not more—reveals to him that the combination cannot be 6, 6, and 1 but must be 9, 2, and 2.

(This, as you have no doubt realized by this time, is nothing more complicated than a variation of No. 17. I include both because the principle involved seems to me uncommonly interesting.)

CHAPTER III

1.

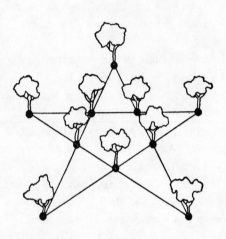

2. Make two vertical cuts at right angles to each other along the diameters and a horizontal cut through the middle of the cake.

3.

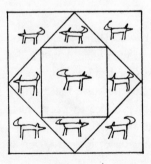

4.

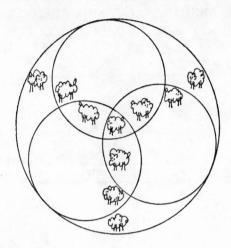

5.

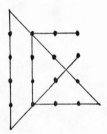

6. Since each dot is actually more than just a point, they can be connected as follows:

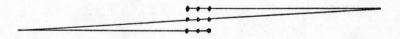

7. There are 35 triangles. In alphabetical order, they are: ABC, ABD, ABE, ABF, ABG, ABH, ACD, ACE, ACI, ADE, ADH, AEF, AEG, AEI, AFG, BCD, BCE, BCG, BCH, BCJ, BDE, BDF, BEJ, BGH, CDE, CDH, CDI, CDJ, CEG, CHJ, DEF, DEI, DEJ, DIJ, and EFI.

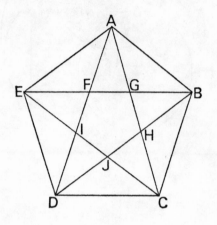

8.

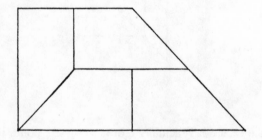

9.

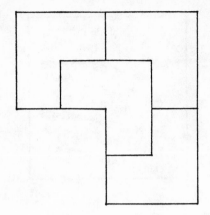

10. The grooves are cut diagonally, as shown:

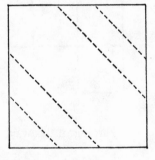

The block slides apart diagonally.

11.

CAN YOU DRAW A PERFECT
SQUARE HAVING ONE DOT
ON EACH OF ITS 4 SIDES
BUT NO SIDE IS TO TOUCH
ANY OF THE WORDS WHICH
ARE PRINTED HEREIN? IT IS
NOT AS EASY AS IT MAY
APPEAR AT FIRST GLANCE.

12.

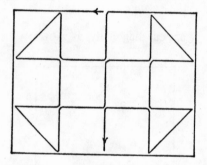

13. Cut the square and rearrange it this way:

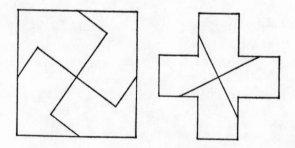

186

14. Ten inches. Since the path of each pursuer is at all times perpendicular to the path of the pursued, no component of the pursued bug's path moves it closer to or farther from the pursuing bug. The pursuing bug will thus catch up with the pursued bug in exactly the same time it would have taken if the pursued bug had remained stationary. The length of the spiral path is therefore exactly the same as the side of the square, ten inches.

CHAPTER IV

1. The categories are as follows: AMTUVWY (symmetry about the vertical axis); BCDEK (symmetry about the horizontal axis); FGJLNPQRSZ (no symmetry); and HIOX (symmetry about both axes).

2. *Witchcraft.*

3. Frederick's message, translated reads: *Dix nez (Dinez) avec moi à cent sous six (Sans Souci)*, or "Dine with me at Sans Souci." Voltaire replies: *G grand, à petit (J'ai grand appétit)*, or "I have a large appetite."

4. Although the paragraph contains 100 words, the most common letter in the English language—*e*—doesn't appear even once.

5. *Eerie.*

6. *Latchstring.*

7. The letters are *und.* The word is *underground.*

8. "I understand you undertake to undermine my undertaking."

9. *Facetiously* and *abstemiously.*

10. *Indivisibility.*

11. Chances are they haven't. For further confirmation, you might try another short spelling test. It consists of only five words —*kimono, naphtha, iridescent, inoculation,* and *rarefy*—and is in my opinion the toughest brief spelling test ever devised by the mind of man. Even professional editors and writers rarely get more than two or three of the five words right.

12. *Unfortunates—u* as in *view, n* as in *know, f* as in *tough, o* as in *beau, r* as in *myrrh, t* as in *pthisis, u* as in *ewe, n* as in *comptroller, a* as in *neigh, t* as in *light, e* as in *tea,* and *s* as in *psalm.*

13. *Stretched.*

14. *Plague.* Remove the first two letters and it becomes *ague.*

15. Water. (H to 0, or H_2O)

16.

$$10200\,4180$$

(I ought to owe nothing for I ate nothing.)

17. *newsstand, sycamore, subpoena, persimmon, awkward, archeology, perhaps, sovereignty.*

CHAPTER V

1.
$$\begin{array}{r} 15 \\ 36 \\ +47 \\ \hline 98 \\ +2 \\ \hline 100 \end{array}$$

2. Since one of the terms is $(x-x)$, which equals zero, the answer is zero.

3. The ship is 28 years old. The boiler is 21 years old.

4. The flagpoles are right next to each other.

5. Five, one, and ninety-four, respectively. The answer can be arrived at by starting with these two equations:

$$10C=3S+0.5P=100$$
$$C+S+P=100$$

Because there are two equations but three variables, the problem cannot, of course, be solved without some trial and error. The easiest way is to try different values for C, since the possibilities are more limited than for S and P.

6. $1.19—a half dollar, a quarter, four dimes, and four pennies.

7. The cost of the room was $27 minus $2.00, or $25. The error comes from mistakenly adding $27 and $2.00 and getting the misleading figure of $29. Many readers will recognize this as one of the oldest puzzles around. I include it here because, judging by the numbers of people who write me about it, its vigor remains undiminished in its old age.

8. The problem can be solved in a number of ways. For example, it can be solved somewhat cumbersomely this way: $1+(2\times3)+(4\times5)-6+7+(8\times9)=100$. Or, a bit more neatly: $(1\times2)+34+56+7-8+9=100$. The most elegantly economical solution, however, appears to be this one: $123-45-67+89=100$. If you still haven't had enough, there are also at least two others.

9. He added his own camel to the original 17, making the division easy:

$\frac{1}{2}\times18=9$

$\frac{1}{3}\times18=6$

$\frac{1}{9}\times18=2$

Since the total is 17, the wise man was then able to take back his own camel and ride on.

10. Square each side:

$$X+\sqrt{X+\sqrt{X+\sqrt{X\ldots}}}=4$$

If, as the problem states—

$$\sqrt{X+\sqrt{X+\sqrt{X\ldots}}} = 2$$

—then X+2=4.
Therefore X=2.

11. $14—the $6.00 he paid for the watch and the $8 in good money he gave the customer in change. The $20 is of no consequence, since the genuine $20 that the jeweler returned to the storekeeper was offset by the $20 in change that the storekeeper gave the jeweler.

12. Six—five from the original twenty-five cigar butts, and one more once he has smoked the five cigars. L. Y. Wu points out, incidentally, that the hobo can make the six cigars from only twenty-four cigar butts if he first borrows one butt, then returns the last butt to the lender.

13. John has seven apples. Paul has five.

14.
```
   888
    88
     8
     8
   +8
 1,000
```

15.

CHAPTER VI

1. The match.

2. No. It's against the law to bury live people.

3. The third error is that there are only two errors.

4. The one that is not a quarter is a dime. The other one, of course, is a quarter.

5. Fold the edge of the paper as shown:

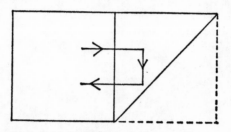

Then unfold it and complete the figure:

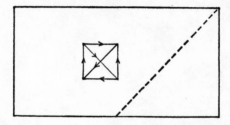

6. No, it isn't legal for a man to marry his widow's sister. Dead people aren't allowed to marry.

7. Of course they have a Fourth of July in England. It's just not a holiday.

8. You don't bury survivors.

9. Moses didn't take any animals onto the ark. Noah did.

10. Put one lump in the first cup, one in the second, and twelve —a very odd number indeed—in the third.

11. All twelve months have twenty-eight days. Some, of course, have more than that, too.

12. Electric trains don't have any smoke.

13. Two—one on each side.

CHAPTER VIII

1. *d*

2. *b*

3. *b*

4. *a*

5. *d*

6. *a*

7. *b*

8. foot

9. *b*

10. *c*

11. *a*

12. *e*

13. *b*. Only Czechoslovakia is landlocked.

14. *a*

15. *c*

16. *c*

17. *d*

18. *a*

19. *a*

20. *b*

21. Barbara has forty, Betty has twenty-four, and Joy has sixteen.

22. *c*

23. *d*

24. *d*

25. *d*

Key to the Mensa test: If you scored more than 24 points, you're definitely Mensa material; from 21 to 23 points, you're very likely Mensa material; from 18 to 20 points, you're a possibility but not a certainty for Mensa; from 15 to 17, you're above average but probably not Mensa material; below 14, see Chapter VIII for puzzle-solving hints.